JEFF KINNEY'İN DİĞER KİTAPLARI

Saftirik'in Günlüğü

Saftirik'in Günlüğü 2: Rodrick Kuralları

Saftirik'in Günlüğü 3: Tırınun Son Örneği

Saftirik'in Günlüğü: Kendin Yap Kitabı

Saftirik'in Günlüğü 4: İşte Şimdi Yandık

Çeviri: Kenan Özgür

SAFTİRİK Greg'in Günlüğü
AMA BU HAKSIZLIK!

Orijinal Adı: Diary Of a Wimpy Kid: The Ugly Truth
Yazarı: Jeff Kinney
Genel Yayın Yönetmeni: Meltem Erkmen
Çeviri: Kenan Özgür
Düzenleme: Gülen Işık
Düzelti: Fahrettin Levent
Kapak Uygulama: Berna Özbek Keleş

22. Baskı: Nisan 2016

ISBN: 978-9944-82-386-9

Baskı ve Cilt: Mimoza Matbaacılık
Davutpaşa Cad. No: 123 Kat: 1-3 Topkapı-İst
Tel: (0212) 482 99 10 (pbx)
Fax: (0212) 482 99 78
Sertifika No: 33198

Yayımlayan:
Epsilon Yayıncılık Hizmetleri Tic. San. Ltd. Şti.
Osmanlı Sk. Osmanlı İş Merkezi No: 18 / 4-5 Taksim/İstanbul
Tel: 0212.252 38 21 pbx Faks: 252 63 98
İnternet adresi: www.epsilonyayinevi.com
e-mail: epsilon@epsilonyayinevi.com
YAYINEVİ SERTİFİKA NO: 12280

TOMAS'A

EYLÜL

<u>Perşembe</u>

Eski en iyi arkadaşım Rowley Jefferson ile büyük kavgamızı edeli nerdeyse iki buçuk hafta oldu. Doğrusunu söylemem gerekirse, onun şimdiye kadar sürüne sürüne bana geleceğini sanıyordum; ama nedense böyle bir şey olmadı.

Birazcık endişelenmeye başladım; çünkü birkaç güne kadar okullar açılacak. Biz de bu arkadaşlığı yeniden yoluna koyacaksak, bir an önce bir şeyler olması lazım. Eğer Rowley ile aramızdaki her şey bittiyse, çok kötü olur, çünkü ikimiz güzel güzel anlaşıp gidiyorduk.

7

Artık arkadaşlığımız tarihe karıştığına göre, ben de yeni bir en iyi arkadaş arayışı içerisindeyim. Ama sorun şu: Şimdiye kadar bütün vaktimi Rowley için harcadığımdan, onun yerini almak için kuyrukta bekleyen kimse yok.

Bu noktada iki seçeneğim var: Christopher Brownfield ve Tyson Sanders. Ama bu çocuklardan ikisinin de kendine göre sorunları var.

CHRISTOPHER   TYSON

Yazın son birkaç haftası Christopher ile takıldım. Daha çok kendisi tam bir sivrisinek mıknatısı olduğu için yaptım bunu. Ama Christopher okul arkadaşından çok yaz arkadaşı olabilir.

8

Tyson fena biri değil; ikimiz aynı bilgisayar oyunlarını seviyoruz. Ama pisuarı kullanırken pantolonunu aşağı kadar indiriyor. Bunu görmezden gelebilir miyim bilmem.

Bundan başka benim yaşıtım olan ve hiç arkadaşı olmayan tek kişi Fregley. Ama onu da en iyi arkadaş adayları arasından çıkaralı uzun zaman oldu.

Her neyse, ben her ihtimale karşı Rowley için kapıyı aralık tutuyorum. Ama eğer bu arkadaşlığı korumak istiyorsa, hızlı davransa iyi eder.

Çünkü böyle giderse otobiyografimde pek hoş görünmeyecek kendisi.

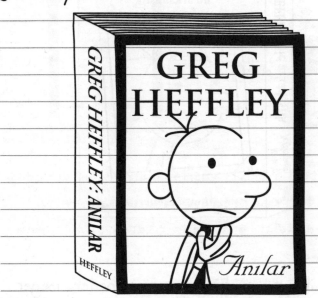

8. BÖLÜM

ÇOCUKLUK

Eskiden bir çocuk tanıyordum.
Adı Rupert miydi Roger mıydı neydi.

Şansım biraz yaver giderse, zengin ve ünlü olacağım. Rowley de YİNE peşimden gelmenin yollarını arayacak.

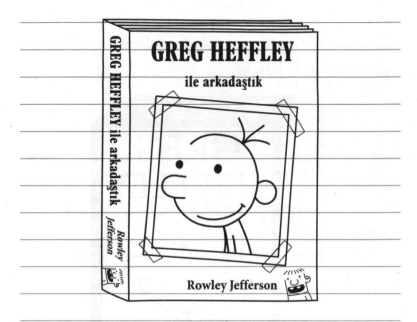

GREG HEFFLEY
ile arkadaştık

Rowley Jefferson

Cumartesi

Rowley ile aramın düzelmemesinin nedeni meğer benim yerime başka bir arkadaş bulmasıymış. Daha doğrusu, ona bu arkadaşı ANNE BABASI bulmuş.

Geçen birkaç hafta boyunca, Rowley, Brian adındaki oğlanla takılmış.

Ne zaman Rowley'nin evine gitsem, onu liseye ya da üniversiteye gidiyormuş gibi görünen bir tiple ön bahçede futbol ya da frizbi oynarken görüyorum.

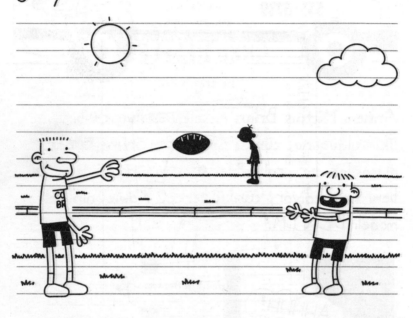

Biraz araştırdım ve Brian denen bu oğlanın mahalleden normal bir çocuk olmadığını öğrendim. Meğer "ağabey kiralama" gibi işler yapan "Müthiş Brian" şirketindenmiş.

Aslında, o çocuğun gerçek adının bile Brian olmadığı konusunda bahse girerim.

Annem Müthiş Brian meselesinin harika bir fikir olduğunu, çünkü çocukların önüne örnek alacakları bir "rol model" koyduğunu söyledi. Bu beni sinir ediyor, çünkü bence, Rowley'nin rol modeli BENİM!

Rowley'nin ailesi, benim yıllarca BEDAVA yaptığım iş için şimdi kalkmış, birine para ödüyor.

13

İşin acıklı yanı, Rowley herhalde ailesinin bu oğlana onunla zaman geçirmesi için para ödediğini bilmiyordur. Gerci Rowley gerçeği bilseydi bile umurumda olacağını sanmam.

Bugün Rowley'nin farklı bir Müthiş Brian ile takıldığını gördüm. Demek sürekli gelen Brian'ın izin günüydü. Rowley'nin bunun farkında olduğunu bile sanmıyorum.

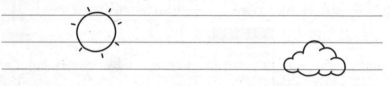

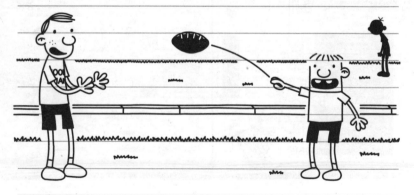

Salı

Bugün okulun ilk günüydü. Büyük konuşmayayım ama görünüşe göre bu yıl benim için harika bir yıl olacak.

Sınıfta bize bu yarıyılda kullanacağımız kitapları dağıttılar. Okulumun yeni kitaplar alacak parası yok; o yüzden hep elden düşme kitaplar dağıtıyorlar.

Ama insanın kendisinden önce on çocuğun okuduğu bir kitabı olunca, öğrenmesi de zor oluyor.

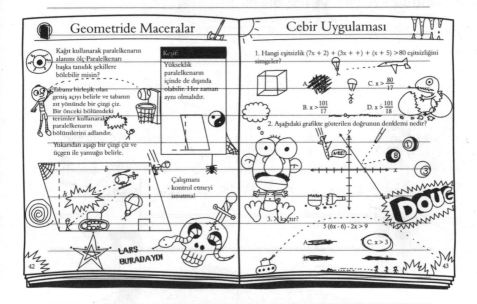

Genellikle, kitapların eski sahipleri söz konusu olduğunda çok şanssızımdır. Geçen yıl, bana eskiden Bryan Goot'a ait olan bir matematik kitabı denk gelmişti.

Bu da benim okuldaki "havama" hiç uymuyordu.

Ama bu yıl şansım döndü. Matematik kitabımı aldığımda, daha önce Jordan Jury'ye ait olduğunu gördüm. Jordon Jury benim bir üst sınıfımın en popüler çocuğu. Bu yüzden bu kitabı taşımak bana ÇOK BÜYÜK popülerlik puanları kazandırabilir.

Jordan'ın bu kadar popüler olmasının nedenlerinden biri, çok büyük ve havalı partiler vermesi. Bu partilere davet edilmek gerçekten çok zor. Ama belki de bu cebir kitabı onun radarına girmek için ihtiyacım olan şeydir.

Popüler çocuklar demişken, bugün öğle yemeğinde Bryce Anderson ve arkadaşlarının yanında oturdum. Bryce da benim sınıfımın Jordan Jury'si. Yanında sürekli onun her söylediğini onaylayan bir sürü kafadarı var.

Bu çocuklar, Bryce onları ne kadar salak durumuna düşürürse düşürsün, ona sadıklar.

Aslında Bryce Anderson en doğrusunu yapıyor. En iyi arkadaşa hiç İHTİYACI yok, çünkü yanında ona tapınan uşakları var. Rowley ile benim yürütememememizin nedeni, arkadaşlığımızda eşit taraflar olmamızdı. Sanırım böyle bir modelin yürüme şansı yok.

Cuma

Bugün okulda Rowley'nin bir çocuğa bu gece rock konserine gideceğini söylediğini duydum. İtiraf ediyorum, biraz kıskandım, çünkü ben hiç gerçek bir rock konserine gitmedim. Ama sahneye kimin çıkacağını öğrenince, davet edilmediğime memnun oldum.

Yine de Rowley'nin benden daha çok eğlenmesine sinir oluyorum. Aslında, bugünlerde HERKES benden çok eğleniyor gibi görünüyor.

Sınıftan bazı çocuklar resimlerini internette yayınlıyorlar.

Hallerine bakılırsa, hepsinin benden daha iyi vakit geçirdiği kesin.

İnsanların benim hayatımın berbat olduğunu düşünmelerini istemiyorum. Bu yüzden benim için her şeyin ne kadar harika olduğunu gösterecek resimler çekmeye karar verdim.

Bir dijital fotoğraf makinen, bir de fotoğraf düzenleyici programın varsa tamamdır. Kendini acayip eğleniyormuş gibi gösterebilirsin.

Bu gece tam müthiş bir yılbaşı partisi ortamı yaratıyordum ki anneme yakalandım.

Annem, fotoğraflarımı internette yayınlamama hayatta izin vermez. "Gizlilik" meselesi filan der. Ya da belki ağabeyim Rodrick'in KENDİ fotoğraflarını yayınlamasına izin verdikten sonra dersini aldığı içindir.

Rodrick kendine yeni bir davul seti almak için işe girmek istiyor ama kimse onu işe almıyor. Annem, son günlerde işverenlerin işe alacakları kişileri araştırdıklarını, Rodrick'in fotoğraflarının da onun şansını azaltıyor olabileceğini söyledi.

Bunun üzerine Rodrick müzik grubuyla olan
fotoğraflarını kaldırıp yerine şunu koydu:

Çarşamba

Bu yıl sınıftaki herkes İleri Sağlık Bilgisi
dersi almak zorunda. Derste, bazı gizli bilgiler
verilecek. Şimdiye kadar bunları öğrenmeye hazır
olmadığımızı düşünüyorlardı sanırım.

İlk birkaç derste kızlarla erkekler bir
aradaydı. Ama bugün Hemşire Powell bizi
ayıracağını söyledi. Kızları Bayan Gordon'ın
odasına gönderdi ve biz erkeklere izletmek için
bir film koydu.

Anladığım kadarıyla film en az otuz yıllıktı. Eminim babam da benim yaşımdayken aynı kaseti izlemiştir.

Filmde gösterilen her şeyi anlatmak istemiyorum çünkü kesinlikle iğrençti. Bana soracak olursanız, bazı şeyler kesinlikle sınıfta gösterilmemeli.

Rowley filmi sonuna kadar izleyemedi bile. İkinci dakikada, "terleme" sözcüğünü duyduğunda uyudu.

Doğrusunu söylemem gerekirse, Rowley'nin böyle şeylere hazır olup olmadığını bilmiyorum. Daha küçük bir çocuk gibi. Bir keresinde bana okuldaki büyük çocuklardan uzak durduğunu, çünkü kendisine "ergenlik" bulaşmasından korktuğunu söylemişti.

Aslında, şimdi düşünüyorum da, Müthiş Brian'ı bir süredir görmedim. Acaba Rowley, bulaşıcı hastalığı olduğunu düşünüp ondan da mı uzak durmaya karar verdi?

Geçen yılki Sağlık dersinde de sigara konusu işlenirken benzer bir şey olmuştu. Öğretmen, size kimin sigara ikram edeceğini bilemeyeceğinizi, bunu en iyi arkadaşınızın bile yapabileceğini söylemişti.

Rowley, bunu duyduktan sonra bir AY boyunca, benimle caddenin aynı tarafında bile yürümedi.

İnanın bana, sigaranın kötü bir şey olduğunu bir öğretmenden duymama gerek YOK.
Büyükbabam geçen yıl Şükran Günü'nde beni bu konuda ikna etti.

Her neyse, sanırım Rowley olgunlaşıp akıllanma konusunda herkesin birkaç yıl gerisinden gelecek çocuklardan biri. Daha ayakkabılarını bağlamayı bile bilmiyor çünkü her şeyi cırt cırtlı.

CIRRRTT

Geçen yıl annesi Rowley'ye bağcıklı ayakkabılar aldı. Onunla kaç kez uğraşmak zorunda kaldığımı hatırlamıyorum bile!

Sanırım en iyi arkadaşımın benim ayakkabılarımın bağcıklarını bağlamayı bilmemden etkilenmesi bir uyarı işareti olmalıydı.

Perşembe
Bugün gazetedeki karikatürleri okuyordum. Birden bir ilan dikkatimi çekti.

Tatlı Meltem Dondurması'nın ilanıydı ve belli ki kendilerine yeni bir yüz arıyorlardı.

Tatlı Meltem'in reklamları televizyonda sürekli gösteriliyor. Reklamlarda çilli ve cırtlak sesli bir çocuk oynuyor.

Tatlı Meltem Çocuğu eskiden çok şekerdi ama yıllar geçtikçe biraz kartlaştı.

Bu yüzden sanırım onun yerini alacak birini arıyorlar.

Bu rol tam BENLİK! Bir kere, ben dondurmaya BAYILIRIM; bu yüzden rolümü yapmam hiç de zor olmaz. İkincisi, Tatlı Meltem reklamının gerekliliklerini yerine getirmek için okulu bol bol ekebilirim.

Ayrıca benim rol için yaşlanacağımı düşünüp endişelenmek zorunda da kalmazlar; çünkü büyümemi durdurmak için ne gerekiyorsa yaparım.

Görebildiğim kadarıyla önümdeki tek engel, babamın Tatlı Meltem'in televizyon reklamlarından NEFRET etmesi çünkü çocuğu sinir bozucu buluyor. Bu yüzden reklamların yeni yüzü ben olursam babamın pek heyecanlanacağını sanmıyorum.

O çocuk nedense babamın tüylerini diken diken ediyor. Hatta babam, Tatlı Meltem Çocuğu'ndan, Şirincik'ten ettiğinden daha fazla nefret ediyor.

Ne zaman televizyonda Tatlı Meltem reklamını görse, oturup Tatlı Meltem yetkililerine öfkeli bir mektup yazıyor. Onlara reklamların kendisini çıldırttığını, ürünlerini asla satın almayacağını söylüyor.

Birkaç hafta sonra, babama Tatlı Meltem'den cevap geliyor. Hep aynı şeyi yapıyorlar, bedava dondurma için kupon gönderiyorlar.

Bu yıllardır böyle devam ediyor. Eğer bir değişiklik olmazsa, bütün Tatlı Meltem dondurmalarımızı saklamak için ikinci bir buzdolabı almamız gerekecek.

Cumartesi

Dün gece anneme Tatlı Meltem yarışmasından söz ettim. O da bunun "heyecan verici bir fırsat" gibi göründüğünü söyledi. Ama sonra bunu söylerken küçük kardeşim Manny'yi düşündüğü ortaya çıktı.

Daha doğrusu bu sabah annemle Manny beni almadan seçmelere gitmek için yola çıkıyorlardı. Onlara son anda yetiştim.

BENİ BEKLEYİN!

Annem benim Tatlı Meltem Çocuğu olmak istememe şaşırmış göründü. Benim bu rol için "biraz büyük" olabileceğimi söyledi. Önce bunun saçma olduğunu düşündüm ama sonra alışveriş merkezinde rakiplerimi görünce, annemin neden böyle söylediğini anladım.

Yine de jüriyi etkileyip işi alabilirdim. Üstelik bir avantajım vardı; başvuranlar arasında bir kağıtta yazanları okuyabilen tek çocuk bendim.

Kuyrukta yaklaşık iki yüz çocuk vardı. Eğer işi almak istiyorsam, dikkat çekici bir numara yapmalıydım. Ben de, Tatlı Meltem sloganını okurken havaya zıplayıp topuklarımı birbirine vurmaya karar verdim.

Ancak sonunda sıra bana geldiğinde, işler planladığım gibi yürümedi.

Jüridekiler beni adımı bile sormadan dışarı çıkarınca, rolü alma şansımın pek yüksek olmadığını anladım.

Fırsatı kaçırıyordum, ben de şansımı artırmak için yapabileceğimi yaptım.

Ama görünüşe göre, işi benden daha küçük bir çocuk alacak. Çok sinir bir durum!

Üstelik bu benim yaşım yüzünden ilk elenmem değil. Geçen ekim ayında, Rowley ile yerel haber kanalının Kırmızı Elma Çiftliği'ne geleceğini, kabak eken, korkuluk filan yapan çocukları çekeceğini duymuştuk.

Bunun televizyona çıkmak için büyük bir fırsat olacağını düşündük. Kendimizi haber kameralarının önüne attık ve gösteriye başladık.

Ancak beş saniye sonra, haberciler bizi sepetlediler.

Sonra bizim yerimize daha küçük çocuklar
getirdiler. O çocuklar da Rowley ile benim
yaptıklarımızın aynısını yaptı.

Tabi o gece o çocuklar haberlere çıktılar.

Aslında uzun zamandır böyle şeyler oluyor. En
kötüsü de kendi ailemde oluyor.

Sekiz ya da dokuz yaşına kadar, aile
toplantılarının yıldızı bendim. Hiç kimse bana
doyamıyordu sanki.

Ama Manny doğduktan sonra benim için işler değişti.

Çocukken kimse seni bir son kullanma tarihin olduğu konusunda uyarmıyor. Bir gün sana bayılıyorlar, ertesi gün bayat pasta gibi davranıyorlar.

Galiba Rodrick'in neden bu kadar huysuz olduğunu anlayabiliyorum. O ilgi merkezi olmaktan çıkalı çok uzun zaman oldu. Üstelik giderek şirinleştiği filan da yok.

Şanslı olan biri varsa o da Rowley. Kendisi tek çocuk, bu yüzden en azından başka bir çocuğun gelip onun yerini almasından endişelenmesine gerek yok.

Pazartesi

Bu gece yemekte babam, kardeşi Gary Amca'nın, kız arkadaşı Sonja ile nişanlandığını söyledi. Bu müthiş bir haber olmalıydı sanırım ama Gary Amca daha önce üç kere evlendi ve ailemiz de buna alıştı. Hatta, evde büyüme tabloları bile kullanmıyoruz; çünkü Gary Amca'nın düğün fotoğraflarına bakarak ne kadar büyüdüğümüzü takip edebiliyoruz.

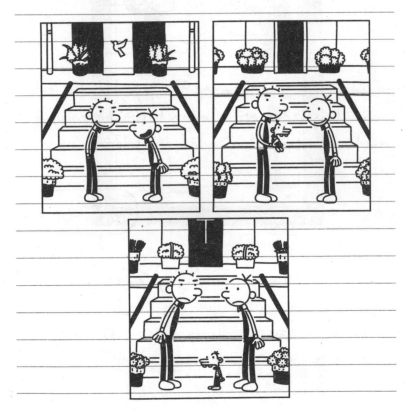

Bu yüzden galiba herkes heyecanını kaybetti. Gary Amca üçüncü kez evlendiğinde, annem onun şöminenin üzerinde duran ikinci düğün fotoğrafını değiştirmeye bile zahmet etmedi. Amcamın yeni karısının kafasını eskisinin üzerine yapıştırdı.

Gary Amca fena bir adam değil aslında. Sadece ilişkilere kendini çok çabuk kaptırıyor. İlk karısı Linda ile tanıştıktan iki ay sonra nişanlanmıştı. Linda, evlendikleri güne kadar onun ne iş yaptığını bile bilmiyordu.

Gary Amca'nın ikinci karısı Charlene'in de, ikinci randevularındaki bir yanlış anlama yüzünden onun çok parası olduğunu sandığını duymuştum.

Meğer Gary Amca'nın kırk beş BİN değil, sadece kırk beş doları varmış.

Ama Charlene düğünde orkestranın parasını ödeme vakti gelene kadar bunu bilmiyordu.

Babam hep Gary Amca'nın artık "büyümesi", çocuk gibi davranmaktan vazgeçmesi gerektiğini söyler. Ama ben babamın yerinde olsam, çoktan umudumu kesmiştim.

Salı

Gary Amca'nın düğününün kasımda olacağını, törenin de geçen sefer olduğu gibi büyük büyükannem Gammie'nin evinde yapılacağını öğrendim.

Gammie doksan beş yaşında ama hâlâ doğup büyüdüğü büyük evde yaşıyor. Kendisi, bütün Heffley ailesinin resmi başkanı gibi.

HEFFLEY AİLE TOPLANTISI

(GAMMIE)

Gammie, dünyada hâlâ mektup yazan ender insanlardan biri. Üstelik size mektup yazdığında, sizden de CEVAP yazmanızı bekliyor.

Gammie'ye benim yaşındaki insanların artık üzerinde pul ve iade adresi olan mektuplar yazmadıklarını filan açıklamaya çalıştım ama beni dinlemek bile istemedi.

Gary Amca'nın son düğününde bana bir mektup kâğıdı ile üzerinde kendisinin adresiyle pul olan bir zarf uzattı. Böylece mektup yazmamak için hiçbir bahanem kalmayacaktı.

G. HEFFLEY
12. SURREY CADDESİ

GAMMIE HEFFLEY
38 BACON CADDESİ
DOĞU V

Sevgili Gammie,

Sevgiler,
Gregory

46

Ama ben hâlâ mektup kâğıdını doldurup ona postalamadım. Bu yüzden ne zaman odamdaki çalışma masasının yanından geçsem, kendimi suçlu hissediyorum.

Gammie, HEP insana kendini suçlu hissettirir zaten. Geçen yıl Şükran Günü'nde, onun iskemlesine osuruk yastığı koydum. O da üzerine oturdu.

Birkac gün sonra, ailedeki herkese Gammie'den bir özür mektubu geldi.

Sevgili Ailem,

Bu mektubu ailemizin Şükran Günü için toplanmasından kısa bir süre sonra meydana gelen talihsiz olay nedeniyle özür dilemek için yazıyorum. Yaşlandıkça, vücudumu kontrol etmem daha zor oluyor. Sanırım son ameliyat da benim küçük "kaçırmalarıma" katkıda bulundu. Umarım her şeyiyle çok güzel ve ayrıcalıklı olan o güne dair aklınızda sürekli kalacak olan şey bu talihsiz olay olmaz.

Sevgiler,
Gammie

Bazen Gammie herkesle kafa mı buluyor ve böyle şeyleri bilerek mi yapıyor diye düşünüyorum. Geçen Paskalya'da bütün aileyi evine davet etti. Ama herkesin başka planları vardı, bu yüzden hiç kimse gitmedi.

Gammie Paskalya sabahı babamı aradı ve bir piyango bileti almış olduğunu, büyük ikramiye olan on milyon doları kazandığını söyledi. Haber aile arasında hızla yayıldı. Çok geçmeden herkes Gammie'nin evinde toplanmıştı.

Ama sonra bilete aslında ikramiye filan çıkmadığı anlaşıldı.

BÜTÜN SAYILARIN AYNI OLMASI LAZIM, GAMMIE.

ANLADIM.

Gammie, milyoner olmadığı için pek de üzülmüşe benzemiyordu. İçimden bir ses onun ASIL istediğini zaten elde ettiğini söylüyordu.

Umarım ben de doksan beş yaşına kadar yaşarım. Çünkü eğer yaşarsam, emin olun, ben de insanlarla kafa bulacağım.

Kasımda Gammie'nin evine gidecek olmak beni biraz geriyor çünkü "Konuşma"yı dinleme sırası bende. Gammie ailede benim yaşıma gelen herkesi oturtuyor ve bir sürü şey anlatıyor. Sanırım büyüklüğüne, bilgeliğine dair şeyler filan.

Gammie'nin "Konuşma"sını dinleyen son kişi Rodrick idi; şimdi sırada ben varım. Gary Amca'nın nişanı bozmasını umuyorum, böylece oraya gitmek zorunda kalmayız. Çünkü bu olayı düşündükçe sinirlerim bozuluyor.

Perşembe
Okulda Bayan Mackelroy adında yeni bir matematik öğretmenimiz var.

Eskiden anaokulunda öğretmenmiş. Ortaokul çocuklarına ders vermeye pek bayıldığını sanmıyorum.

Matematik dersi beden eğitimi dersinden hemen sonra; bu yüzden Bayan Mackelroy'un sınıfına girdiğimizde, herkes ter içinde oluyor.

Bayan Mackelroy müdüre şikâyette bulundu ve sınıf "maymun kafesi" gibi kokarken ders anlatamayacağını söyledi. Müdür de bundan sonra beden dersinden sonra duş yapmak zorunda olduğumuzu bildirdi.

Sınıftaki oğlanların çoğunun bu karara gıcık olduğunu söyleyebilirim.

Bundan rahatsız olmayan tek kişi Roger
Townsend idi. O da iki kere sınıfta kalmış; bu
yüzden artık koca adam sayılır.

Biz geri kalanlar, numara yapmak zorunda
kalacağımıza karar verdik. Dün beden eğitimi
dersi bitince, hepimiz sırayla saçlarımızı ıslattık.
Böylece duş almış gibi GÖRÜNDÜK.

Bayan Mackelroy'u kandırabildik mi bilmiyorum ama oğlanların soyunma odasına girip araştırmaya kalkacağını hic sanmam.

Bu duş alma meselesi bana yazın, Rowley ile hâlâ arkadaşken olan bir şeyi hatırlattı. O zamanlar hemen her gün Rowley'nin evine gidiyordum. Ama sorun, her defasında Fregley'nin evinin önünden geçmek zorunda kalmamdı.

Rodrick'in, bir insanın bizim evden tepenin zirvesine kadar bütün yolu drenaj borusunun içinde sürünerek gidebileceğini söylediğini hatırladım.

Onun haklı olup olmadığını görmeye karar
verdim. İster inanın ister inanmayın haklıydı.
Drenaj borusunun içi çok karanlık ve kötüydü;
ama Fregley'den kurtulmak için borunun içinde
sürünmeye değerdi.

Eve dönerken, yine drenaj borusunun içinden
geçtim.

Ama ön bahçede hortumla filan yıkansam iyi olurmuş; çünkü ben içeri girince annem şüphelenmiş göründü.

Annemin, benim drenaj borusunun içinden geçtiğimi öğrenirse çok kızacağını biliyordum. Bu yüzden bir şey söylemedim. Ama annem bana yemekten önce duş almam gerektiğini söyledi. Banyodan çıktığımda, yatağımın üstünde bir şey duruyordu.

Paketi açtım. İçinden bir deodoranla bir kitap çıktı.

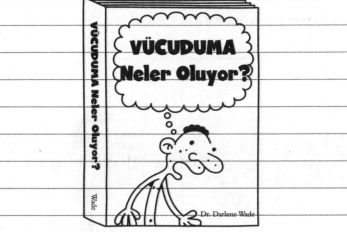

Deodoranı şifoniyerimin üzerine koydum ama kitabı çöpe attım. O kitabı daha önce görmüştüm. Rodrick benim yaşımdayken, annem aynı kitaptan ona da almıştı. Ben de kitabı Rodrick'in ıvır zıvır çekmecesinde bulmuştum. İnanın bana, kitaptaki resimleri bir kez daha görmeye hiç ihtiyacım yok.

İşin daha da kötüsü, annem o hafta beni yerel gazetedeki ebeveyn köşesinin konusu yaptı. Gerçek adımı vermedi ama kimden söz ettiğini anlamak için dedektif olmak gerektiğini sanmıyorum.

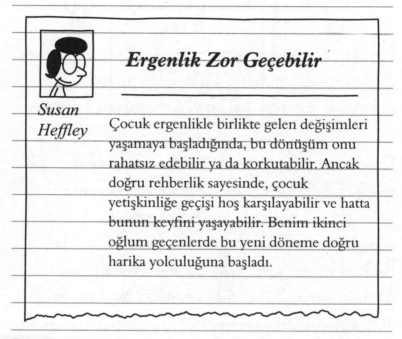

Ergenlik Zor Geçebilir

Susan Heffley

Çocuk ergenlikle birlikte gelen değişimleri yaşamaya başladığında, bu dönüşüm onu rahatsız edebilir ya da korkutabilir. Ancak doğru rehberlik sayesinde, çocuk yetişkinliğe geçişi hoş karşılayabilir ve hatta bunun keyfini yaşayabilir. Benim ikinci oğlum geçenlerde bu yeni döneme doğru harika yolculuğuna başladı.

Pazar

Bu gece annem bir "ev toplantısı" düzenledi. Bunu ne zaman yapsa, hiç iyi şeyler olmuyor. Düzenlediği son toplantıda, banyonun durumundan yakınmıştı.

Biz bir türlü "hedefi tutturamadığımız" için tuvaletin çevresini temizlemek zorunda kalmaktan bıktığını söyledi.

Ben de onun neden söz ettiğini çok iyi biliyordum. Bir keresinde, tuvaleti Manny'den sonra kullanmak zorunda kaldığım için otobüsü kaçırdım.

Tek söyleyebileceğim şey şu: Bu soruna neden olan ben değilim. Rodrick tuvaleti kullanırken çoğunlukla ışığı yakmıyor.

Annem yeni bir kural koyduğunu, bundan sonra biz oğlanların tuvaleti kullanırken, ne olursa olsun, oturmak zorunda olduğumuzu söyledi.

Ama BU fikir hiçbirimizin hoşuna gitmedi.
Rodrick, iki pisuar almamızı önerdi ve biz
erkeklerin sayıca ANNEMDEN fazla
olduğumuzu söyledi. Üstelik böylece tuvaleti bir
anda birden fazla kişi kullanabilirdi.

Ama annem "Daha neler!" dedi ve Rodrick'in bu
fikrine karşı veto hakkını kullandı.

Bu geceki ev toplantısının da tuvalet
toplantısının uzantısı olacağını düşünüyordum.
Çünkü hiç kimse oturma kuralına uymuyor
ve durum eskisinden beter. Ama bu geceki
toplantının konusu tamamen farklıydı.

Annem bize okula dönmeye karar verdiğini ve haftada birkaç ders görmeye başlayacağını söyledi.

Bu habere hazırlıksız yakalandım. Okuldan eve HER dönüşümde annemi evde buluyorum ve bu hoşuma gidiyor.

Ama annem yıllarca evde çocuklarla çalıştıktan sonra, kendi zihnini uyaracak bir şeyler yapmaya ihtiyaç duyduğunu söyledi. Yarım dönem ders alacak ve nasıl gittiğine bakacakmış.

Sanırım annemin neden dışarı açılmak istediğini anlayabiliyorum. Ben de onun her gün yaptığı şeyleri yapsam, herhalde kafayı yerdim.

Annem & Ben DANS DERSİ

Annem biz erkeklerin haftada birkaç akşam kendi yemeğimizi hazırlamak zorunda kalacağımızı ve onun yaptığı işleri yapmaya başlayacağımızı söyledi.

Bu işlerden biri öğle yemeği hazırlamak. Doğrusunu söylemek gerekirse, bu işin bize kalmasından mutluyum.

Annem her gün yemek çantamıza bir not yapıştırıyor. BU olmadan yaşayabileceğimden eminim.

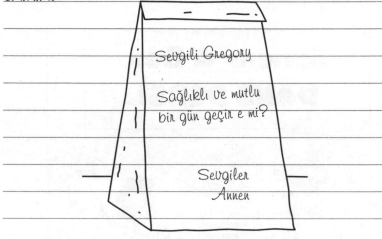

Sevgili Gregory

Sağlıklı ve mutlu bir gün geçir e mi?

Sevgiler
Annen

Çarşamba

Evet, annemsiz geçirdiğimiz ilk birkaç akşam tam bir felaketti. Pazartesi akşamı, kendi başımıza yemek hazırlamaya çalıştık ama hiçbirimiz ne yaptığımızı bilmiyorduk.

Manny buzlu çay hazırlamakla görevliydi ama çayı çıplak elleriyle karıştırdığı için, içmek mümkün değildi.

ŞIK
ŞIK

Rodrick de rostoyu pişirecekti ama eti fırına koymadan önce üzerindeki plastik ambalajı çıkarmayı unutmuş.

BU ET NEDEN PARLIYOR?

Biz de ev yemeği fikrinden vazgeçtik ve yemek yemek için dışarı çıktık. Restorandan çıktığımızda, Rodrick ağzındaki sakızı etrafta uçuşan pervanelere doğru tükürdü ve yanlışlıkla babamı vurdu!

TUUU

Babam otoparkın çevresinde Rodrick'i kovaladı ama Rodrick çok hızlı koştuğundan ona yetişemedi. Sonra ayağı yerdeki bir şeye takıldı ve bileğini burktu.

Rodrick babamı acil servise götürmek zorunda kaldı. Doktor, babama bileğini nasıl incittiğini sorunca, babam önüne bakmadığını ve Manny'nin yerdeki kamyonlarından birine basıp düştüğünü söyledi.

Babamın neden gerçeği söylemediğini anlayabiliyorum. Bir keresinde ben de bileğimi kırmış ve herkese yumruk kavgasında kırıldığını söylemiştim. ASLINDA tuvalette çok uzun süre oturduğum için ayaklarım uyuşmuştu ve kalkmaya çalışınca düşmüştüm. Ama diğer hikâye daha çok hoşuma gitmişti.

Daha annemsiz birkaç gün geçirdik ve işler sarpa sarmaya başladı bile. Şimdilik tek bir ciddi yaralanmamız var ama kim bilir daha neler olacak.

Perşembe

Spagetti Cenneti'nde arta kalan yemeklerimizi paket yaptırıp eve getirmiştik. Bu akşam yemeğinde bunları yedik. Babam geç saate kadar çalışmak zorundaydı. Bu yüzden Rodrick'i aradı ve ona herkesin makarnasını mikrodalga fırında ısıtmasını söyledi.

Rodrick önce benim tabağımı verdi ve verirken de dedi ki:

Soğusun diye bir süre makarnaya üfledim. Ama Rodrick'in aslında benim makarnamı mikrodalga fırında ısıtmadığını, sadece numara yaptığını bilmiyordum.

Köfteyi ısırdığımda, BUZ gibiydi.

Bu deneyimden sonra bir daha tabakta kaldığı için paketletilen yemekleri yiyebilir miyim bilmiyorum.

Üstelik öğle yemeği işi de yolunda gitmiyor.
Bu hafta öğle yemeklerimizi hazırlama sırası
Rodrick'teydi. O da annem gibi yemek çantama
not yapıştırmış.

Rodrick'i bir kez bile ellerini yıkarken
görmediğim için, sandviçi yeme zahmetine bile
katlanmadım.

Benim bu haftaki işim çamaşırdı. Vardiyamın bir an önce bitmesi için sabırsızlanıyorum. Bir çocuğun annesinin iç çamaşırlarını katlamak zorunda kalması, yasalara bile aykırıdır bence!

Cuma

Annemin okula gitmesinin yarattığı en büyük değişikliklerden biri, artık ödevlerimde bana babamın yardım etmesi. Babama bir garezim yok ama annem ödevler konusunda babamdan KAT KAT iyiydi. Annem bana yardım ederken nerdeyse bütün cevapları söylüyor, ben de ödevimi on dakika içinde bitiriyorum.

Babamla her şey çok farklı. O bana ödevi NASIL yapacağımı öğretmeye çalışıyor. Bu da dünyanın zamanını alıyor. Üstelik babam okulu bitireli çok uzun zaman olmuş. Bu yüzden oturup onun kitapları okumasını ve anlamasını beklemek zorunda kalıyorum.

Ama en KÖTÜSÜ matematik. Galiba bugünlerde matematiği öğretme yöntemleri babamın çocukluğunda olduğundan çok farklı. Babam, yeni kuralları hiç anlamıyor ve bunlara kızıyor. Bana da kendi bildiği yöntemleri öğretmeye çalışıyor.

Babam bir de sayfaları daha kolay çevirmek için işaret ve baş parmağını yalıyor. O bunu yaptığında, çevirdiği sayfaları aklımda tutuyorum ve onun tükürüğüne dokunmuyorum.

Ama o kadar sayıyı kafamda tutunca, matematikle ilgili bilgilere yer kalmıyor.

Yanlış bir şey yaptığımda hemen anlıyorum çünkü babam bana kızıyor ve burnundan hızlı hızlı solumaya başlıyor. Bu yüzden Cebir çalışırken koluma bir elbezi koymaya başladım.

Ödevler bittiğinde, aradan iki saat geçmiş ve benim yatma vaktim gelmiş oluyor. Tek söyleyebileceğim şey şu: Umarım annem derslerini çok çabuk halleder çünkü ben akşamları gerçekten televizyon izleme ihtiyacı duyan bir insanım canım.

Pazartesi

Matematik iyice sorun olmaya başladı. Bizim okulda "standartlaştırılmış sınav" yapılacakmış ve duyduğuma göre eğer biz iyi puanlar almazsak öğretmenler de ikramiye alamayacaklarmış. Bu yüzden çocukların üzerinde çok büyük bir baskı var, bu da çok fena. Hatırlıyorum da, anaokulundayken matematik ne kadar EĞLENCELİYDİ.

Bayan Mackelroy diyor ki: eğer sınavda başarılı olamazsak bütçemiz kesilirmiş, müzik dersleri de yapılmazmış filan... Ama çocukların bu mesajı aldıklarını sanmıyorum. Birkaç hafta önce matematik sınavımız vardı. Bayan Mackeroy "defterlerin kitapların açık" olacağını söyledi. Yani bize yardımcı olması için defterlerimizi ve kitaplarımızı kullanabilecektik.

Sonra kendisi bir şeyle ilgilenmek için sınıftan çıktı. O çıkar çıkmaz da ortalık karıştı.

Hemen herkes sınavda zayıf not aldı çünkü insanlar defter kâğıtlarını cephane olarak kullanıyorlardı.

Bu örneğe bakarak düşünüyorum da, Bayan Mackelroy ikramiyesini nasıl harcayacağı konusunda büyük planlar yapmasa iyi olur bence.

EKİM

Salı

Bu gece, ben kanepede otururken babam yanıma geldi. Canı bir şeye sıkılmış gibiydi. Bana, neden kendisinin benden istediğini yapıp sabahleyin geri dönüşüm kutusunu dışarı çıkarmadığımı sordu.

Ona herhalde kafasının karıştığını, benden kesinlikle böyle bir şey istemediğini söyledim. Ama o da bunu önceki akşam ben bilgisayarda oyun oynarken istediğini söyleyip ısrar etti. Doğrusunu söylemek gerekirse, hatırlar gibi oldum.

Eğer GERÇEKTEN unuttuysam, bu benim suçum değildi. Benim hatırlamak konusunda HARİKA bir sistemim vardır.

Biliyorsunuz, bazı insanlar bir şey hatırlamaları gerektiğinde kendilerine notlar yazarlar. Ben bunun boşuna zahmet ve kâğıt israfı olduğunu düşünüyorum.

Bu yüzden, diyelim ki yataktayım ve annem gelip sabahleyin okula izin kâğıdı götürmem gerektiğini söylüyor. Yataktan çıkıp not yazmıyorum.

Sadece yastıklarımdan birini odanın öbür ucuna
fırlatıyorum.

Sonra sabah kalktığımda, kapıdan
çıkmak üzereyken yastığı görüyorum ve
"Hoppala, yastığım burada ne arıyor?" diye
düşünüyorum.

Sonra aklıma geliyor. "Ah, evet, okula izin kâğıdı götürecektim." Ne demek istediğimi anladınız mı? Acayip kolay ve mükemmel bir sistem.

Şimdi düşünüyorum da, geri dönüşüm kutusu için kendime bir not HAZIRLAMIŞTIM aslında. Sabah kalktığımda unutmayayım diye, yatmadan önce çoraplarımı televizyonun üzerine koymuştum.

Eğer babam sistemimi karmakarışık edecek bir şey yaptıysa, sucu kendinde arasın.

Ama babam işin peşini bırakacak gibi değildi. Artık büyüdüğüme göre, sorumluluklarımın farkına "biraz daha" varmam gerektiğini söyledi.

Daha önce de babamdan böyle şeyler duydum. Yazın son birkaç haftasında, komşumuz Bayan Grove kendisi iş gezisindeyken bitkileriyle ilgilenmem için beni işe aldı. İlk birkaç gün bunu yaptım ama sonra, tahmin edebileceğiniz gibi, başka şeylerle meşgul olmam gerekti.

Babam bana bitkilerin ne durumda olduğunu sorduğunda, en azından bir HAFTADIR oraya gitmediğimi fark ettim. Bitkileri sulamaya gitmek için, Bayan Grove'un anahtarını almaya gittim. Ama anahtar her zamanki yerinde yoktu.

Evin altını üstüne getirip anahtarı aradım ama bulamadım.

Meğer anahtarı bulamamamın nedeni, bizim evde olmamasıymış. Bayan Grove'un evinde bırakmışım. O da seyahatten dönünce bulmuş.

Bayan Grove anahtarı kapıda bulunca çok öfkelendi. Ama bana kalırsa, evi soyulmadığı için sevinmeliydi.

Bitkileri yüzünden de çok sinirlendi çünkü maalesef birçoğu ölmüştü. Ona, belki de yaşamak için fazla suya ihtiyaç duymayan kaktüs ya da ona benzer bitkiler almasının daha iyi olacağını söyledim.

Böylece, BİR DAHAKİ sefere kendisi iş seyahatine gittiğinde anahtarını kaybedersem, hiç sorun olmazdı.

Ama Bayan Grove bundan sonra beni ölse işe almayacağını söyledi. Sonra da beni paramı ödemeden eve gönderdi. Bu çok fena oldu çünkü o anahtarı ararken dünya kadar zaman harcamıştım.

Her neyse, sanırım babam bu olayı unutmadı. Bu yüzden ondan yine "sorumluluk" ile ilgili laflar duydum.

Umarım babam bir dahaki sefere çoraplarımı televizyonun üzerinden kaldırmaz ve işler bu noktaya varmaz.

80

<u>Perşembe</u>

Babam benim daha fazla sorumluluk almam konusunda gayet ciddi. Yapmamı istediği ilk şey de sabahları kendi kendime uyanmaya başlamam.

<u>Bu</u> gerçek bir sorun; çünkü beni mutlaka <u>ONUN</u> uyandırması gerekiyor.

Bu YILLARDIR böyle. Şimdi değiştirmeye ne gerek var anlamadım ki.

Babam, eğer çalar saatle kendi kendime uyanıp kalkmayı öğrenemezsem, yüksekokula gittiğimde de bunu yapamayacağımı söyledi.

Ama ben hep babamla bu sayede iletişimde kalacağımızı düşünmüştüm.

Dün ilk kez kendi kendime uyanıp kalkmaya çalıştım ama pek başarılı olduğum söylenemez. Saat çaldı ama ben sesi rüyamda duyuyorum sandım.

Bugün de pek farklı değildi. Çalar saati "radyo"ya ayarladım ve bir klasik müzik kanalı seçtim. Çünkü sabahın köründe o sinir bozucu dıt sesini duymak istemiyordum. Ama müzik de beni uyandıramadı

Sorun şu: Beni bir insanoğlu uyandırmadığı sürece, beynim uyumaya devam etmek için bir bahane buluyor mutlaka. Ama sanırım bu çalar saat meselesi için bir çözüm geliştirdim. Bugün malzeme odasında, şu eski kurmalı saatlerden bir tane buldum. Bu saatler çalmaya başladığında ortalığı ayağa kaldırıyor.

Saatin çalışıp çalışmadığını kontrol ettim. Hem de nasıl çalışıyordu!

ZIIIIRRRRRRR

Böyle bir sesi duyan hiç kimsenin uyuyabileceğini sanmıyorum. Tek sorun şu: Saatin bir "erteleme" tuşu yok. O yüzden kapatıp uyumaya devam edeceğimden korkuyorum.

Ben de bu gece saati yatağımın altına sakladım. Böylece, çaldığında onu bulmak için kalkmak zorunda kalacağım. Sonra da bütün gün ayakta olacağım.

Cuma
Yeni çalar saatin bazı yeni sorunlara neden olduğu ortaya çıktı.

Yatağımın altında kurmalı saatle, kendimi
patlamaya hazır bir bombanın üzerinde uyur
gibi hissediyordum. Bu stres yüzünden gecenin
yarısını uyanık geçirdim.

Okulda da gözlerim yarı kapalı gezdim.
Toplantı yapılana kadar bir sorun yoktu. Bizi
oditoryumda sıraya dizdiler. Ben de duvara
yaslandım.

Yarım saniye kadar uyumuş olmalıyım. Çünkü
elim kaymış ve ben yanlışlıkla yangın alarmını
çalıştırmışım.

Bütün okulu boşaltmak zorunda kaldılar.
Üç dakika sonra da okulun önünde itfaiye
kamyonları bitti.

Yangın filan olmadığını öğrenince, herkesi
tekrar okula soktular. Müdür mikrofonu aldı
ve alarmı devreye sokan her kimse okuldan
uzaklaştırılacağını, gidip kendisinin itiraf etmesi
gerektiğini söyledi.

Çok şey bilmiyor olabilirim ama şu kadarını biliyorum: İnsanlardan suçlarını itiraf etmelerini istemeden ÖNCE cezanın ne olacağını söylememelisiniz. Ben de susmanın ve ortalığın sakinleşmesini beklemenin daha akıllıca olacağına karar verdim.

Üçüncü dersten sonra ortalığa bir söylenti yayıldı. Yangın alarmı, kolu çektiğinizde görünmez bir sıvı püskürtüyormuş. Öğretmenlerde de birinin elinin üzerindeki sıvıyı görmek için kullandıkları özel bir X-ray değneği varmış. Yani suçluyu bulmaları an meselesiymiş.

Sonra herkes bu söylentiyi ÖĞRETMENLERİN yayıp yaymadığını merak etmeye başladı. Belki de bu ilk önce hangi çocuğun tuvalete gidip ellerini yıkayacağını görmek için bir numaraydı.

Böylece herkes GERÇEKTEN paranoyak oldu.

HİÇ KİMSE tuvalete gitmedi. Gerçekten gitmesi gerekenler de tuvaletlerini günün sonuna kadar tutmaya karar verdiler.

Müdür sonunda okulu erken tatil etmek zorunda kaldı. Çünkü kimse ellerini yıkamıyordu ve grip mevsiminin tam ortasındayız!

Annem ders çalışmak için kütüphaneye gitmişti. Ben de işyerinden babamı aramak ve gelip beni okuldan almasını söylemek zorunda kaldım. Buna pek de sevinmedi.

Ama eğer sabah kendi kendime kalkmak zorunda olmasaydım, bunların hiçbiri yaşanmayacaktı.

Çarşamba

Sağlık dersinde, "Hayatın Gerçekleri" adında yeni bir ünite başlatıyorlar. Görünüşe göre bu, son iki aydır anlattıkları bütün konuları kapsıyor. Evlerimize izin kâğıtları gönderdiler. Eğer izin kâğıdın imzalanmazsa, dönemin geri kalanı boyunca derse girmene kesinlikle izin verilmiyor.

Şu izin kâğıdı meselesinden hiç hoşlanmıyorum. Annem benim sadece çocuk filmleri izlemem için izin veriyor, bu yüzden derslere girmeme ASLA izin vermeyeceğinden eminim.

Bu sorunu halletmek için, sahte bir not yazdım ve asıl izin kâğıdının üzerine yapıştırdım.

Çocuğumun fazladan ev ödevi yapmasına izin veriyorum.

Velinin imzası

Neyse ki annem kâğıda çok yakından bakmadı. Ben de ihtiyacım olan imzayı aldım.

NE KOLAY BİR KARAR!

Bu "Hayatın Gerçekleri" ünitesini işledikleri için gerçekten çok memnunum; çünkü bu konularla ilgili sormak istediğim bir sürü soru var ama güvenilir cevapları nereden alabileceğimi bilmiyorum.

Konuyla ilgili bildiğim hemen her şeyi Albert Sandy'den öğrendim. Onun da kafamı yanlış bilgilerle doldurup doldurmadığını merak etmeye başladım. Mesela geçen hafta, öğle yemeğinde herkese bir kızın osurmasının tıbbi açıdan imkânsız olduğunu söyledi.

Ben, annemle Dorothy Teyze'yi Noel'de kucaklaşırken gördüğüm için, bunun doğru olmadığını biliyorum.

ZART

Her neyse, bugün "Hayatın Gerçekleri" ünitesinin ilk günüydü. Tabii Hemşire Powell velisi izin kâğıdını imzalamayan çocukları bugünün "özel yardımcıları" olmaları için kütüphaneye gönderdi.

Biz geri kalanlar ise çok heyecanlıydık. Hemşire Powell'in bize anlatacağı ilginç şeyleri duymak için sabırsızlanıyorduk.

Ama HİÇ DE beklediğim gibi olmadı. Hemşire Powell tahtaya şemalar astı ve "zigot"lardan, "kromozom"lardan, başka bir sürü bilimsel saçmalıktan söz etmeye başladı.

Hâlâ onun bize bütün bunların kocaman bir şaka olduğunu söyleyip asıl konulara geçmesini bekliyordum. Ama böyle bir şey olmadı.

Sanırım okul, ilgimizin kaybolması için kafamızı karıştırmaya çalışıyor sadece.

Her neyse, eğer okul GERÇEKTEN bizim kafamızı karıştırmaya çalışıyorsa, bunu gayet iyi başarıyor. Öğle yemeğinde, "Hayatın Gerçekleri"nde öğrendiklerimizi izin kâğıtlarını imzalatamayan çocuklara anlatmaya çalıştık ama tek bir noktada bile anlaşamadık.

<u>Cumartesi</u>

Annem okula dönmeye karar verdikten sonra, babamın yeni bir görevi daha oldu: Biz çocukları dişçi randevularına götürmek!

Çoğu çocuk dişçiye gitmeyi sevmez ama ben bunu DÖRT GÖZLE bekliyorum. İki yaşımdan beri aynı dişçiye gidiyorum. Tam bana göre!

♥ **Yumuşak Dokunuşlar** ♥

♥ *Pediatrik Diş Bakımı* ♥

Korkaklar Bizim İşimiz!

Yüksek Çamlar Alışveriş Merkezi

Fıstık

Ama dişçiye gitmeyi sevmemin asıl nedeni, orada çalışan hijyen uzmanı Rachel'a SIRILSIKLAM âşık olmam.

Rachel bana sürekli diş fırçalamak ya da diş ipi kullanmakla ilgili öğütler veriyor. Ama o kadar tatlı ki onu ciddiye almak çok zor.

Annem de diş ipi kullanmam konusunda başımın etini yiyor. Eğer dişlerime daha iyi bakmazsam, üniversiteye başlamadan protez kullanmak zorunda kalacağımı söylüyor.

Aslında düşünüyorum da, takma diş takmak belki o kadar kötü bir şey değildir.

Takma diş takarsam, dişlerimle bir BAŞKASI ilgilenebilir. Ben de kalan zamanı keyif alacağım şeyler yaparak geçirebilirim.

İnsanın hijyen uzmanına âşık olmasının en kötü tarafı, onu altı ayda bir dişlerini temizletmeye gittiğinde görebilmesi. Bu yüzden her ziyareti çok iyi değerlendirmek zorundayım.

Son randevumda, Rachel'a onunla ne kadar ilgilendiğimi göstermek için, dişlerim temizlenirken sürekli gözlerinin içine baktım.

Bu sabah da dışarı çıktım ve Rachel üzerinde ekstra iyi izlenim bırakmak için kolonya satın aldım. Babam bana arabaya binmemi söylediğinde hazırdım.

Ama babam dişçinin muayenehanesinin önünden geçti ve otoyola çıktı. Ona dönüşü kaçırdığını, Yumuşak Dokunuşlar Diş Bakım Merkezi'nin diğer tarafta kaldığını söyledim.

Babam ise benim artık çocuk dişçisine gidemeyecek kadar büyüdüğümü, bugünden itibaren beni kendi dişçisi Dr. Kagan'a götüreceğini söyledi.

Bu ismi duyunca tepeden tırnağa ürperdiğimi hissettim. Dr. Kagan'ın reklamlarını otoyol kenarında görmüş ve onun Yumuşak Dokunuşlar'dan çok farklı bir yaklaşıma sahip olduğu izlenimime kapılmıştım.

DR. SALAZAR KAGAN
AĞIZ CERRAHİSİ
ve genel dişçilik

KANAL TEDAVİ
APSE TEDAVİSİ
KEMİK YÜKLEME

"Çünkü kötü ağız sağlığı insanı gülümsetmez."

Babamın fikrini değiştirmesini sağlamaya çalıştım ama o beni yeni dişçiye götürme konusunda bütün formaliteleri hallettiğini, bu işin geri dönüşünün olmadığını söyledi. Kaçmayı düşündüm ama babam aklımdan geçenleri tahmin etmiş olmalı ki arabanın kapılarını kilitledi.

Dr. Kagan'ın muayenehanesi gözümde canlandırdığımdan daha korkutucuydu. Yumuşak Dokunuşlar'ın bekleme salonundaki boyama kitaplarından, oyuncaklardan orada hiç yoktu.

Dr. Kagan beni muayenehanesinde bekliyordu. İçeri girdiğimde bütün sivri aletlerinin ve makinelerin ortada olduğunu gördüm.

Adamın hiç şakası yoktu besbelli.

Koltuğa oturduğumda, Doktor Kagan benim yeme ve içme alışkanlıklarımı deşmeye başladı. Ona kola içtiğimi söyleyince ÇILDIRDI. Sonra yan odaya geçti ve içinde çürük bir dişin olduğu kahverengi sıvıyla dolu bir kavanoz getirdi.

Yirmi dört saat boyunca kola dolu kavanozda bekletilen gerçek dişin bu hale geldiğini söyledi. Ben de Doktor Kagan'a dişlerimi asla bütün bir gece kola dolu bir kavanozda bırakmayacağımı söyledim. Alaycı davrandığımı düşündüğünden eminim. Oysa ben sadece ilgilendiğimi ve kendisini dinlediğimi göstermeye çalışıyordum.

Sonra dişlerimi temizledi. Paniğe kapılmaya başladım, çünkü size kızmasını hiç istemediğiniz biri varsa, o da elindeki metal aletleri ağzınızın içinde dolaştırıp duran adamdır.

Sonra Doktor Kagan röntgen çekmeye başladı. Dişlerimin arasına bir parça plastik koydu ve bana ısırmamı söyledi. Sonra röntgeni çekti ve bir sonraki plastik parçasını hazırladı.

İki ya da üç röntgenden sonra, duruma alıştım. Doktor Kagan azı dişlerimle ilgilenirken, o bana söylemeden plastiği ısırdım. En azından plastiği ısırdığımı SANDIM; çünkü ısırdığım plastik değil, Doktor Kagan'ın parmağıymış.

Daha önceki öfkesi bunun yanında HİÇBİR ŞEY idi!

Doktor Kagan bana kendisi benim sonuçlarım üzerinde çalışırken bekleme salonuna gitmemi söyledi. Onun sırf benimle hesaplaşmak için gelip babama dişime kanal tedavisi yapılması gerektiğini filan söyleyeceğinden emindim.

Ama Doktor Kagan daha da beter bir şey yaptı. Babama, ağzımdaki kapanış bozukluğu için "önemli düzeltici önlemler" alınması gerektiğini söyledi ve şu broşürü verdi:

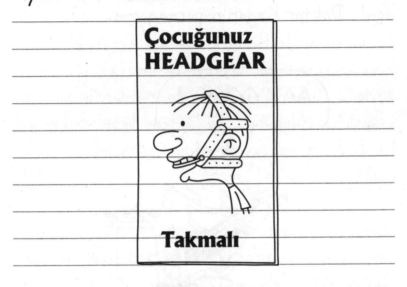

Çocuğunuz
HEADGEAR

Takmalı

"Headgear" ağız ve çene bozukluğunu düzeltmek için takılan bir şeymiş. Ben de adını "ağızlık" koydum. Bunu sürekli, özelikle gündüzleri okuldayken takmam gerekiyormuş. Adam besbelli benim sosyal hayatımı mahvetmeye çalışıyor.

<u>Pazartesi</u>

Bu sabah uyandığımda, ağızlığımı bıraktığım yerde bulamadım. Ben de okula onsuz gitmek zorunda kaldım. Bundan şikâyetçi olduğum filan yok.

Sağlık dersinde Hemşire Powell ebeveynlik konusunda yeni bir üniteye başlayacağımızı söyledi. Anne ya da baba olmanın büyük bir sorumluluk olduğunu, bu ünitede bebek bakımının hiç de kolay bir şey olmadığını göreceğimizi anlattı.

Sonra bir karton yumurta çıkardı. Her birimiz kendi yumurtamızı akşam eve götürecek, ertesi gün de okula geri getirecekmişiz.

Kural şu: Geri getirdiğimiz yumurtanın kusursuz olması, üzerinde çatlak filan olmaması gerekiyor.

Tavuk yumurtasıyla bebeğin ne ilgisi var anlamadım. Bu da annemle babam beni özel okula gönderselerdi daha mı iyi eğitim alırdım diye düşündüğüm durumlardan biri.

Hemşire Powell bu yumurta işinin notlarımızın %25'ini oluşturacağını söyledi.

Hemşire Powell notlardan söz edince, çok gerildim. Zaten matematiğim zayıf, bir de Sağlık dersinden çakmak istemiyorum. Bu yüzden yumurtama gözüm gibi bakacağımdan emindim.

Dersten çıktıktan sonra olanlara bakılırsa, diğer oğlanların KENDİ notlarını kafaya takar gibi bir halleri yoktu.

Duyduğuma göre, hademe dolaplardaki yumurta sarılarını kazımak için bütün öğleden sonra uğraşmış.

Benim dışımda yumurtasını kırmayan tek kişi yumurtayı gömleğinin cebine sokan Rowley idi.

Benim gömlek cebim ya da yumurtamı koyabileceğim başka bir güvenli yerim yoktu. Hemen bir şeyler düşünmek zorundaydım.

106

Tuvaletten kocaman bir rulo tuvalet kâğıdı aldım ve sırt çantamın içine minder gibi yerleştirdim. Yumurtayı ezmesinler diye kitaplarımdan bazılarını çıkarmak zorunda kaldım. Bu da bu gece tarih ödevimi yapamayacağım anlamına geliyor sanırım.

Geçen yıl yaşadığım bir olaydan dolayı yumurtalar beni çok geriyor.

Ailem yine Snellaların çocuklarından birinin yarı yaş günü partisi için onların evine davetliydi. Snellalar masayı bir sürü yiyecekle donatmışlardı ve yiyeceklerin birçoğu benim için fazla süslüydü. Ama annem, tabağıma bir şeyler almazsam kabalık etmiş olacağımı söyledi.

Masada bana tanıdık gelen tek yiyecek, mayonezli yumurta dilimleriydi. Büyükannemin evinde iki kez bunlardan yemiştim çünkü.

Tabağıma on dilim yumurta aldım. Ama birini ısırınca, kusacak gibi oldum. Snellaların evindeki dilim yumurtaların tadı, büyükannemin evindekilere HİÇ benzemiyordu. Ama ne yazık ki tabağım bu yumurtalarla doluydu.

Ben de hiç kimsenin bakmadığı bir anı kolladım. Sonra da bütün yumurta dilimlerini yemek odasındaki plastik bitkinin dibine boşalttım.

FOŞ

Böylece durumu idare ettim.. Ama birkaç hafta sonra, Bayan Snella anneme evlerinde berbat bir koku olduğunu, nereden geldiğini de bir türlü bulamadıklarını söylemiş.

Bay ve Bayan Snella önce kokunun halıdan geldiğini sanmışlar, bu yüzden gelip halıyı şampuanla yıkaması için bir temizlikçi tutmuşlar. Ama bu sorunu çözmemiş. Onlar da duvarlardan birinde sincap ya da fare öldüğünü düşünmüşler. Bu kez de cesedi bulması için marangoz çağırmışlar.

Birkaç hafta sonra, kokuya daha fazla dayanamamış olmalılar ki, taşındılar.

İtiraf etmeliyim, onların plastik bitkiyi de yanlarında götürdüklerini görünce, kendimi biraz suçlu hissettim.

O zamandan beri, Fregley'nin evine nasıl gizlice yumurta dilimi sokabileceğimi düşünüp duruyorum.

Salı

Dün eve geldiğimde, yumurtamı çorap çekmeceme koydum. Ama sonra orada güvende olmayacağını fark ettim.

Ne zaman yeni bir şeyim olsa, Manny onu bulup canına okuyor.

110

Manny'nin benim ağızlığımı bulması da sadece iki buçuk gün aldı. Doktor Kogan'ın ne dediği umurumda değil. O ŞEYİ bir daha dünyada ağzıma sokmam!

Yumurtayı dolabımın en üstüne saklamayı düşündüm ama bu da Manny'yi durduramazdı. Daha önce çizgi romanlarımı saklamıştım oraya ama çocuk maymun gibi tırmanabiliyor.

Sonunda saklamak için ne kadar uğraşırsam, Manny'nin bulma olasılığının o kadar arttığını fark ettim. Ben de yumurtamı onun bakmayı asla akıl edemeyeceği çok açık bir noktaya saklamaya karar verdim.

Yumurtayı buzdolabının ikinci rafına koydum. Ama bu sabah yumurtamı almak için buzdolabını açtığımda, onun bıraktığım yerde olmadığını gördüm.

Paniğe kapıldım. Anneme Manny'yi yumurtamı dolaptan alırken görüp görmediğini sordum.

Ama annem yumurtayı KENDİSİNİN aldığını ve bana onunla kahvaltı hazırladığını söyledi.

Birden, içimin bir tuhaf olduğunu hissettim. Madem bir yumurtaya yirmi dört saat göz kulak olamıyordum; nasıl ebeveyn olacaktım ben?

Okula gittiğimde, Sağlık dersine giren bütün kızların KENDİ yumurtalarını sağ salim getirdiklerini gördüm. Kızların bazıları yumurtalarını diktikleri küçük keselerde taşıyorlardı. Birkaçı da yumurtasını simlerle, pullarla filan süslemişti.

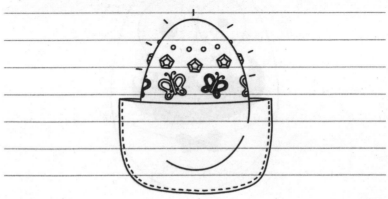

Dersin amacının bize bebek bakmanın ne kadar zor olduğunu öğretmek olduğundan eminim. Bu yüzden kızların mesajı doğru aldıklarını sanmıyorum.

Rowley'nin bakmadığı bir sırada onun yumurtasını alıp benimmiş gibi göstermeyi düşünüyordum. Ama yumurtanın üzerine pastel boyalarıyla resim yaptığı için bu mümkün değildi.

KÜÇÜK ROWLEY

Hemşire Powell masama geldiğinde, içinde sahanda yumurtamın olduğu küçük poşeti açtım ama pek etkilenmiş görünmedi.

Böylece sanırım Sağlık dersini tekrarlamak için yaz okuluna devam etmem gerekecek.

Hemşire Powell dünden beri yumurtalarını mükemmel bir şekilde koruyan herkesi tebrik etti. Sonra da yumurtaların hepsini toplayıp çöpe attı.

Bunu gören Rowley ve kızlar ağlama krizine girdiler.

Söyleyebileceğim tek şey şu: Bu olay ülkemizde bir sonraki kuşak anne babalar konusunda ciddi ciddi endişelenmeme neden oldu.

Cuma
Bugün öğleden sonra kapı çaldı. Gidip açtım ve karşımda büyükbabamı görünce çok şaşırdım.

Kafam da karıştı çünkü yanında küçük valizi vardı. Sonra dönüp de annemle babamı da ellerinde valizlerle görünce neler olup bittiğini anladım.

Annemle babam uzun süredir baş başa zaman geçiremediklerini, bu yüzden de evden uzakta "romantik bir hafta sonu" geçirmeye karar verdiklerini söylediler. Büyükbabamdan da onların yokluğunda gelip bize göz kulak olmasını istemişler.

Keşke gitmek zorunda olmasalar ve "romantik" lafını da hiç etmeselerdi. Çünkü bu kadar bilgi bana çok fazla geldi.

Annemle babam Rodrick'le beni evde yalnız bırakmayı göze alamıyorlar. Çünkü bunu en SON yaptıklarında, Rodrick büyük bir parti vermişti.

Annemle babam ne zaman bir yere gitseler, bizi büyükanneme bırakırlar. Ama büyükannem de şu anda arkadaşlarıyla bir gemi yolculuğunda; bu yüzden bizi büyükbabama emanet etmek zorunda kaldılar.

Annemle babam giderken bize önceden haber vermezler. Evlilik yıldönümlerinde, gittikleri yerden telefon edene kadar hiçbir şeyden haberimiz bile yoktu.

Bizi en son büyükbabama bıraktıklarında, Rodrick ve ben çok küçüktük. O hafta ne felaketler yaşanmıştı, tam hatırlamıyorum. Ama büyükbabamın beni yanlış saat yanlış antrenmana bıraktığını hatırlıyorum.

Rodrick'in büyükbabamın bize bakıcılık yapması fikrinden pek hoşlandığını sanmıyorum. Çünkü annemle babam gider gitmez, o da sıvıştı.

Ne yazık ki benim minibüsüm de ehliyetim de yok. Bu yüzden büyükbabam ve Manny ile birlikte eve tıkılıp kaldım.

HADİ PİŞTİ OYNAYALIM!

HIŞIR

Manny, daha ikindi vakti saat dört buçuk olmasına karşın doğruca yatmaya gitti. Böylece büyükbabamla ben baş başa kaldık.

Büyükbabam akşam yemeği için alınan ekmeklerle ızgara peynirli sandviç yaptı. Küçüklüğümden beri bu sandviçlerden yememiştim. Biraz televizyon izledik. Ama saat yedide büyükbabam televizyonu kapattı ve bana masal okumasını isteyip istemediğimi sordu. Anaokulu günlerimden beri kimse bana masal okumadı. Ama büyükbabamın kalbini kırmak istemiyordum. Bu yüzden idare ettim.

Cumartesi
Dün gece yedi buçukta yattığımdan, bu sabah çok erken uyandım.

Alt kata indiğimde, mutfak masasının üzerinde büyük, beyaz bir dosya gördüm.

İzgara peynirli sandviçler, masal, erken yatmak... birden hepsinin nedenini anladım. Büyükbabam, annemin bizi ona en son emanet ettiğinde hazırladığı el kitabını kullanıyordu. Sekiz ya da dokuz yıl önceydi bu.

Sayfaları karıştırdım. Tabi küçük birer çocukken bize nasıl bakılması gerektiği konusunda bir sürü talimat vardı.

Bu talimatların en az %95'inin de geçerliliği kalmamıştı.

K Kırmızı meyve suyu

Yatmadan önce Rodrick'e kesinlikle içirme çünkü bu onun aşırı hiperaktif olmasına yol açıyor.

Yazılanlardan bazıları gerçekten utanç vericiydi. Dosyayı Rodrick'ten önce bulduğuma memnunum yoksa dünyayı bana dar ederdi.

S Spor Ayakkabı

Gregory spor ayakkabılarına "sıpa ayakkabı" diyor. Sağ ve solunu ayırt edemediği için ayakkabılarını giyerken yardıma ihtiyacı var.

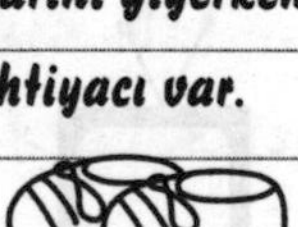

T harfine geldiğimde şununla karşılaştım:

Eğer bol bol televizyon izlememe izin verilmezse, bütün bir hafta sonunu büyükbabamla geçirmeye dayanabileceğimi sanmıyorum. Bu yüzden bu sayfayı çıkardım ve yerine yeni bir sayfa taktım.

123

Sonra S sayfasının T sayfasının arkasında olduğunu fark ettim. Böylece bunu da değiştirmek zorunda kaldım.

S Sopa

Eğer Rodrick evden izin almadan çıkarsa ona sopa atmalısın·

Pazartesi

Ne yazık ki annemle babam dün Rodrick'ten önce eve geldiler. Büyükbabam da huzurevine geri döndü. Yazık oldu, cünkü S maddesinin uygulanması icin dua edip duruyordum.

Annem, hafta sonu boyunca babamla bol bol konuştuklarını, kendisi okula başladıktan sonra evde bir şeylerin aksadığı konusunda fikir birliğine vardıklarını söyledi.

Annemin, üzerimize düşeni yapmadığımız için bizi azarlayacağını sandım. Ama o, temizliğe yardım etmesi için birini İŞE alacaklarını söyledi. Duyduklarıma inanamıyordum. Annem "ev işlerine yardımcı" sözcüklerini kullanmıştı ama ben bunun "hizmetçi" anlamına geldiğini biliyordum.

Galiba annem ev işlerine yardım etmesi için birini tutmuş olmaktan utanıyordu. Bize bunu kimseye söylememizi tembihledi.

İyi de, üzgünüm ama, böyle fırsatlar insanın karşısına sık çıkmıyor. Bu yüzden okulda çenemi tutmam biraz zor oldu:

125

Chirag Gupta kendi ailesinin hizmetçiye İHTİYAÇ duymadığını, her gün okuldan eve gidince annesini evde bulduğu için çok mutlu olduğunu söyledi.

KATIR KUTUR

Ama eminim hizmetçisi olmayan herkes sırf kendini daha iyi hissetmek için böyle söylüyordur.

Yarın hizmetçimiz Isabelle'in ilk günü. Ben, bütün işleri savsaklayabileceğimizi ve ortalığı canımızın istediği gibi dağıtabileceğimizi düşünüyordum, nasıl olsa arkamızdan toplayan biri olacaktı. Ama annem bu gece herkese evi temizletti. Isabella'nın bizim bir "çöp evde" yaşadığımızı düşünmesini istemiyormuş.

VIRIN

126

Salı

Bugün okuldan eve döndüğümde, Isabella salonda oturmuş, sohbet programı izliyordu. Herhalde onu aylaklık etmekle suçlayamam çünkü biz onun yerine bütün temizliği yapmıştık zaten. Ama iki saat boyunca televizyonun karşısından ayrılmadı ve gözünü kırpmadan seyretti.

Bu gece annem okuldan eve döndüğünde, evin tertemiz olduğunu görünce pek şaşırıp sevinmiş göründü. Bütün işi BİZİM yaptığımızı hatırlamadı galiba.

Ama o kadar mutluydu ki keyfini kaçırmak istemedim.

Ben annem kadar mutlu değildim. Dün gece Isabella'ya kirli çamaşırlarımla ilgilenmesi için bir not bıraktım. Bir çocuktan emir alıp almayacağından emin değildim; bu yüzden notu annemin ağzından yazdım.

Sevgili Isabella
Lütfen oğlum Gregory'nin çamaşırlarını yıka.

Saygılar
Bayan Heffley

Teknik olarak kendi çamaşırlarımı KENDİM yıkamak zorundayım ve annemin Isabella'dan bunu benim yerime yapmasını rica ettiğimi öğrenmesini istemiyordum. Bu yüzden en alta şu notu ekledim:

> *Not: Bu notu okuduktan sonra yırtıp at.*

Sonra notu kirli sepetinin üzerine, Isabella'nın görebileceği bir yere koydum. Eve döndüğümde giysilerimi yatağımın üzerinde düzgünce katlanmış bir halde bulmayı bekliyordum ama bunun yerine Isabella'nın karşılık olarak yazdığı NOTU buldum.

İyi ki eve annemden önce gitmişim. Yoksa notu o bulacaktı.

> *Sevgili Bayan Heffley,*
> *Gregory hangi çocuktu?*
>
> *Isabella*

Bu çok sinir bir durumdu çünkü kirli çamaşırlarımı binbir zorlukla üst kata taşımıştım. Bu arada şunu belirteyim, yukarı çıkarmak aşağı indirmekten çok daha zordu.

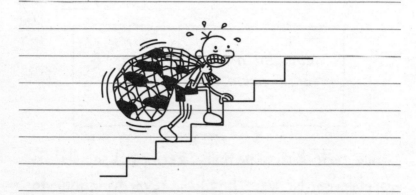

Isabella perşembeye kadar gelmeyecek. Bu yüzden sanırım yeni bir deneme yapmak için o zamana kadar beklemek zorundayım.

Bu benim için çok heyecan verici çünkü bugüne kadar işlerimi yaptırabileceğim kimsem olmadı. Rodrick kendi angaryalarını yaptırmak için HEP beni kandırıyor.

Önce benden bir şey istiyor, ben de hayır diyorum.

Sonra ondan geriye saymaya başlıyor. Neden bilmem, her defasında buna kanıyorum.

Bu tür bir şeyin yetişkinler üzerinde işe yaramayacağını öğrendim.

Geçen hafta babamın televizyonun uzaktan kumandasını getirmesini sağlamaya çalıştım. Çünkü kumandayı masanın üzerinde unutmuştum. Ama kılını bile kıpırdatmadı.

Her neyse, umarım Isabella perşembe günü işimi halleder. Kaç gündür aynı çorapları giyiyorum; mukavvaya döndü çoraplar!

Perşembe
Uf, iş iyice saçmalaşmaya başladı. Dün gece kirli çamaşırlarımı alt kata indirdim ve Isabella'ya yine bir not yazdım.

> Sevgili Isabella,
>
> Gregory, odasının duvar kâğıtları mavi olan çocuk. Lütfen onun giysilerini yıkayıp kurut ve odasına koy.
>
> > Teşekkürler
> > Bayan Heffley

Ama ben temiz çamaşırlar yerine bir not daha buldum.

> Sevgili Bayan Heffley
> Verdiğiniz bilgi için teşekkürler.
> Peki açık renklileri koyu renklilerden ayırayım mı?
> Yoksa hepsini bir arada mı yıkamamı istersiniz?
>
> > Isabella

Isabella'nın derdini anladım. Bu işi böyle uzatmayı düşünüyor. Bir yandan da onun işten kaçma konusundaki becerisine saygı duyuyorum. Ama öbür yandan, bir an önce temiz çamaşırlara ihtiyacım var.

İşin daha da KÖTÜ tarafı, Isabella bizim abur cuburlarımızı yiyor. Bu gece gofret almak için kilere gittim; poşet bomboştu.

Patates cipslerinin de bittiğini fark ettim. Ve, ister inanın ister inanmayın, Isebella kilere abur cubur seçimlerimizden yakınan bir not bırakmış.

Sevgili Bayan Heffley
Lütfen benim sade cipsten çok acılı
olanları sevdiğimi unutmayın.

Isabella

Yediği cipsler ZATEN acılıydı ama bunu anlamamış. Manny cipslerin üzerini yalıyor ve sonra onları yeniden pakete koyuyor. Ne yazık ki ben de bunu pek hoş olmayan bir şekilde öğrendim.

Annem dışarı çıktı ve Isabella için abur cubur aldı. Hepsini kilere koydu. Bizim bunlara el sürmemiz yasak.

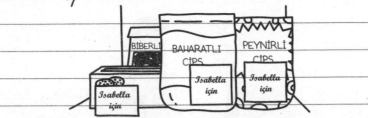

Pazartesi

Bugün okulda müzik programı için para toplamak üzere bir etkinlik düzenleneceğini duyurdular. Adı Şamata olacakmış. Anladığım kadarıyla, kızlı erkekli büyük bir parti olacak. Eh, ben de katılmazsam olmaz.

Benim canımı sıkan tek şey, "refakatçi" meselesi.
Bu yüzden, davetiyeyi anneme gösterirken, o
kısmı kestim.

Salı
Tamam, hizmetçimizden umudumu kestim.
Çamaşırlarımı yıkaması konusunda bir deneme
daha yaptım ama o bunu da geçiştirdi.

Sevgili Isabella
Açık renklilerle koyu renklileri bir arada
yıkayabilirsin·
Gregory'nin okula giderken giyecek bir şeyi
kalmadığı için bu işe öncelik ver lütfen·

Bayan Heffley

Eve döndüğümde kirli sepetinin üzerinde şu
notu buldum:

Sevgili Bayan Heffley
Açık renklilerle koyu renklileri nasıl yıkayacağımı
netleştirdiğiniz için teşekkürler. Ama ne yazık ki
daha önce yazdığınız ve Gregory'nin hangi çocuk
olduğunu söylediğiniz notu kaybettim.

Isabella

Ben de pes ettim. Evi hep Isabella gelmeden önce biz temizlediğimiz için, onun evde yaptığı tek "işin" notlar yazmak olduğundan kesinlikle eminim.

Üstelik durum giderek kötüleşiyor. Bu gece yattığımda, çarşafın altında bir şey hissettim. Alıp bakınca bunun bir külotlu çorap olduğunu gördüm.

Demek Isabella BENİM yatağımda öğlen uykusuna yatıyor. Annemin odasına gittim ve ona Isabella'yı işe almakla hata ettiğini, onu kovması gerektiğini söyledim.

Ama annem dinlemek bile istemedi. Isabella'yı işe aldığından beri evin "bal dök yala" olduğunu, bizim için yaptığı işler nedeniyle ona minnettar olmamız gerektiğini söyledi. Yani Isabella annemi BİR GÜZEL kandırmış.

Tek söyleyebileceğim şey şu: Eğer hizmetçilik bütün gün televizyon izlemek, abur cubur yemek, benim yatağımda öğlen uykusuna yatmak anlamına geliyorsa, sanırım sonunda beni heyecanlandıracak bir iş buldum!

KASIM

Babam dün akşam sekizde Şamata için beni okula bıraktı. İçeri girdiğim anda büyük bir hata yaptığımı anladım. İçerdekilerin %90'ı oğlan, %10'u kızdı. Daha da kötüsü, Rowley de oradaydı.

Hemen çıkmak istedim ama refakatçilerden biri, kapıyı kilitlemişti bile. Böylece, bütün gece diğerleriyle birlikte oraya tıkılıp kaldım.

139

Sanırım bizim sınıftaki kızların çoğu Şamata'ya gelmemeye karar vermiş, GELENLERİN de akılları başlarına sonradan gelmişti.

Olabildiğince iyi zaman geçirmek zorunda olduğuma karar verdim ve oditoryuma girdim. Herkes kendi havasındaydı. Fark ettiğim ilk şey, her çocuğa en az bir yetişkin düştüğüydü. Bu da çılgınca zaman geçirmek için hiç uygun bir durum değildir.

Refakatçilerin çoğu veliydi. Ama birkaç öğretmen de vardı. İçimden bir ses öğretmenlerin de başka şansları olmadığı için orada olduğunu söylüyor.

Eşyalarımı, bütün çocukların olduğu sahneye
bıraktı. Sonra Rowley'nin de orada olduğunu
fark ettim ve eşyalarımı sahnenin öbür ucuna
çektim.

Çocukların çoğu geceden umudunu kesmişti
herhalde. Çünkü hemen herkes yanında getirdiği
elektronik oyuncaklarla oynuyordu.

Ben bilgisayarlı oyunlarımı yanımda getirmeyi akıl
edememiştim. Oyalanacak bir dergim ya da başka
bir şeyim de yoktu. Bu yüzden yetişkinlerden
birine ne yapabileceğimi sordum.

Bayan Barnum, köşede gece boyunca "eğlence
molası" vermek isteyen herkes için bir "faaliyet
merkezi" olduğunu söyledi.

Ama bütün faaliyetler küçük çocuklara göreydi.

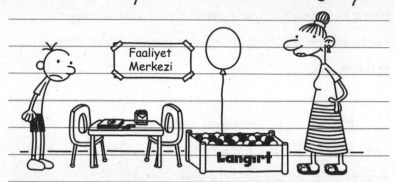

Ben de bunun üzerine ellerim kucağımda, uyku tulumumun üzerinde oturmaya karar verdim.

Saat dokuzda, yetişkinler "parti oyunları" vaktinin geldiğini söylediler. Ama hiç kimse onları duymadı çünkü herkesin kulağında kulaklıklar vardı. Bay Tanner insanların "sosyal" olması gerektiğini söyledi ve herkesin elindeki cep telefonlarını, müzikçalarları filan alıp bir çöp torbasına doldurdu.

Sonra oditoryumun ortasında halka şeklinde oturduk. Bayan Carr birbirimizi daha iyi tanımamıza yardımcı olacak "buzkıran" oyununu oynayacağımızı söyledi.

Ama ortada bir gerçek var. Biz çocuklar birbirimizi zaten çok iyi tanıyoruz çünkü anaokulundan beri beraberiz. Hatta birbirimizi biraz FAZLA iyi tanıyoruz.

Bayan Carr "İsim Oyunu" ile başlayacağımızı söyledi. Herkes kendine asıl adının ilk harfiyle başlayan bir lakap bulacakmış. "Süslü Seth" ya da "Fıttırık Fred" gibi. İddiaya göre, bu lakaplar kişiliğin hakkında fikir veecekmiş.

Önce Rowley başladı.

"RENKLİ ROWLEY!"

Havalı bir lakap bulmak çok zordu gerçekten ve sıra hızla bana geliyordu. Sonunda "Görkemli Greg"de karar kıldım. Bunun biraz tuhaf olduğunu biliyordum ama "G" ile başlayan şık bir lakap bulmak hiç kolay değildi ki.

Sanırım sağımdaki çocuk, George Fleer, da benimle aynı sorunu yaşıyordu.

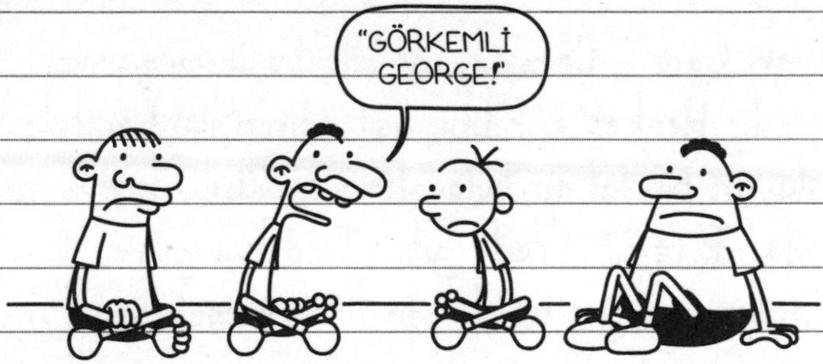

"GÖRKEMLİ GEORGE!"

George ile aynı ismi kullanamazdım çünkü insanlar ondan kopya çektiğimi düşünürlerdi.

Ben de oturup bir süre daha "G" ile başlayan güzel bir sözcük bulmaya çalıştım ama herkes bana bakıyordu ve ben hiçbir şey düşünemiyordum.

Sonunda Bayan Libby bir deneme yapmak için atıldı ve beni kurtardı.

Herkes, "Cici" G ile başlamadığı halde bunu beğenmiş göründü. Bu da insanın eğitim sistemimizden şüphe duymasına neden oluyor çünkü Bayan Libby sekizinci sınıfların İngilizce öğretmeni.

Ben "Cici Greg"in BERBAT bir lakap olduğunu düşündüm ama daha iyi bir isim bulamadan sıra solumdaki çocuğa geçti. İş işten geçmişti artık.

145

Şimdi geceyi bir de aptal bir lakapla geçirmek zorunda kalacaktım. Belki de üniversiteye kadar da bundan kurtulamayacaktım.

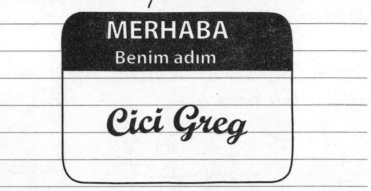

Sonra, "Bunu Daha Önce Hiç Kimseye Söylemedim" adında bir oyun oynadık. Hepimiz bir sırrımızı söylemek zorundaydık. Bayan Carr, bu oyunun birbirimize "bağlanmamızı" sağlayacağını söyledi. Ama bence ASIL amaç, refakatçilerin kimlerin yaramazlık yaptığını öğrenmeleriydi.

Daha sonra Teddy Coldwell koridoru geçip tuvalete gidince ve bir refakatçi de onu takip edince teorimin doğru olduğu ortaya çıktı.

Bir süre daha oyunlar oynadık ama kimse dikkatini oyuna veremiyordu çünkü her beş saniyede bir elektronik eşyalar torbasındaki cep telefonlarından biri titreşiyor ya da çalıyordu. Bay Tanner da çalan telefonu bulup kapatmak için torbanın altını üstüne getiriyordu.

Sonunda pes etti ve torbayı öğretmenler odasına kilitledi.

Oyunlar bittiğinde, bir sonraki faaliyete kadar on beş dakika dinlenme molamız vardı. Birkaçımız yanında abur cubur getirmişti ama dışarıdan yemek getirmek kesin olarak yasaktı. Biz de bunları gizlice yemek zorunda kaldık.

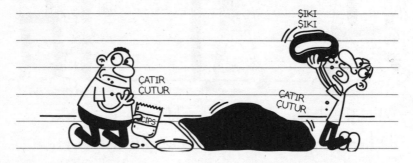

Refakatçiler kimlerin yanında abur cubur getirdiğini BİR BİR biliyordu sanki. Bunların %95'ine el koydular. Bay Farley benim yastık kılıfımın altına gizlediğim baharatlı toplarımı bile buldu.

Sonunda aramızda bir köstebek olduğuna karar verdik. Bu, Justin Spitzer idi ve ödül olarak yetişkinlerin bizden topladığı abur cuburları alıyordu.

Yanında hâlâ abur cubur olan tek çocuk Jeffrey Chang idi. Kocaman bir paket peynirli cipsi vardı. Jeffrey yakalanmasının an meselesi olduğunu biliyordu herhalde. Kendini erkekler tuvaletine kilitlemiş, cipslerinin tadını çıkarmaya çalışıyordu. Ama yetişkinler olup bitenleri fark ettiler. Jeffrey de paniğe kapıldı ve kanıttan kurtuldu!

Moladan sonra yeniden halka olduk. Bayan Dean bize "Bil Bakalım Kim?" adında yeni bir oyun oynayacağımızı söyledi. Sonra bizi takımlara ayırdı. Ben George Fleer, Tyson Sanders ve başka birkaç çocukla Üçüncü Takım'daydım.

Rowley ile aynı takıma düşmediğim için memnundum. Çünkü bundan çok rahatsız olurdum.

Oyun şöyleydi: Her takım yan odaya geçiyor ve üyelerinden birinin resmini çekiyordu. Ama resim çok yakından çekilmeliydi. Yani kulak, burun, el ya da öyle bir şeyin fotoğrafı olmalıydı. Sonra her takım fotoğrafı içeri getirecekti ve diğer takımdakiler bu fotoğraftakinin kim olduğunu bileceklerdi.

Sonra Bayan Dean, kazanan takımın kafeteryanın buzdolabındaki dondurmalı pastaları yiyebileceğini söyledi. İtiraf etmeliyim, eğlenceli bir oyuna benziyordu. Ama Bayan Dean bize fotoğraf makinelerini dağıttığında, ortalık birbirine girdi. Çünkü neredeyse iki saattir hiçbirimiz teknolojik bir alete elimizi sürememiştik.

Sonra bunların fotoğrafı anında çıkaran eski model şipşak makinelerden olduğunu gördük. Herkes biraz hayal kırıklığı yaşadı çünkü bu makinelerin ekranı filan yok.

Bizim takım fotoğrafı gizlice çekmek için fen laboratuarına gitti. Yapmamız gereken ilk şey, kimin resmini çekeceğimize karar vermekti.

George Fleer kendisinin göbek deliğinin fotoğrafını çekmemiz gerektiğini söyledi. Ama herkes bunun cevabı açık etmek olacağını düşündü. Çünkü George'un kocaman bir göbeği var. Diğer gruplar görür görmez tanır ve resimdekinin kim olduğunu anlardı MUTLAKA.

Grubumuzdaki diğer çocukların da fotoğraflarını çekmeye çalıştık ama çoğunun kim olduğu hemen anlaşılıyordu.

Nicky Wood fotoğrafta kendisi olmak istedi. Ama onun da her yeri cille kaplı. Cevabı ele vermeyecek tek bir yerini bile bulamadık.

Christopher Bronfield'in resmini çektik. Ama o sırada Dördüncü Takım'daki çocukların bizi gözetlediğini fark ettik ve başka birini seçmek zorunda kaldık.

Tyson Sanders'in bir sürü resmini çektik ama en iyisi kolunu büktüğü resimdi.

Neyin fotoğrafı olduğu bile anlaşılmıyordu. Biz de oyuna bununla katılmaya karar verdik.

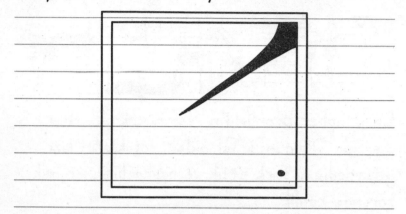

Bütün takımlar yeniden kütüphanede toplandığında, fotoğrafımızı duvara, diğer fotoğrafların yanına astık. Diğer fotoğrafları görür görmez de bizim kazanacağımızı anladık.

Bazı fotoğraftakileri tanımak o kadar kolaydı ki. Bunu çekenlere acıdık neredeyse.

Hatta, Rowley'nin takımındakiler o fotoğrafı çekerken ne düşündüler, anlamak mümkün değil!

Bir an önce oyunun tahmin aşamasına geçmek için sabırsızlanıyorduk. Çünkü bizim fotoğraftakinin kim olduğunu hiç kimsenin anlayamayacağından emindik. Ancak Bay Tanner durmuş, fotoğrafımıza bakıyordu.

Sonra Bay Tanner Üçüncü Takım'ın "çocukça hareketinden" hiç hoşlanmadığını ve bizi yarışmadan diskalifiye ettiğini söyledi.

Bay Tanner'ın neden söz ettiğini anlamak için birbirimize baktık. Ama Bayan Dean de öfkeli görünüyordu. Birinin "posteriyor"unun fotoğrafını çekmemizin kesinlikle yakışık almadığını söyledi.

Takımdaki hiç kimse "posteriyor"un ne demek olduğunu bilmiyordu. Ama neyse ki kütüphanedeydik. Sözlüğü açıp baktık. İnanmayacaksınız ama meğer "popo" anlamına geliyormuş. Bu anlama gelen daha bir milyon sözcük de varmış.

HEE HEE HEE HEE!

Ama öğretmenler çok KIZMIŞTI: Ciddi ciddi bizim birinin poposunun resmini çektiğimizi düşünmüşlerdi. Gerçekten de resim belirli bir açıda tutulduğunda, bu hataya nasıl düştükleri anlaşılabiliyordu.

Bay Tanner velilerimizi arayacağını ve onlardan bizi eve götürmelerini isteyeceğini söyledi. Sonra da resimde poposu görünen çocuğun başının GERÇEKTEN büyük derde gireceğini ekledi.

Bay Tanner gecenin on birinde annemleri ararsa, bunun bizimkilerin hiç hoşuna gitmeyeceğini biliyordum. Diğer bir sürü çocuğun da aynı şeyi düşündüğünü anlayabiliyordum. Sonra George Fleer birden koşmaya başladı. Herkes paniğe kapıldı.

Biz de koşmaya başladık.

Herkes bir yöne dağıldı. Ben kendimi müzik
odasında Tyson Sanders ile saklanırken buldum.
Kimse bizi orada aramaya gelmesin diye ışıkları
da söndürdük.

Tyson, öğretmenlerin popoları kontrol etmelerinden ve resimdeki popoyla karşılaştırmalarından korkuyordu. Ama Tyson'a endişelenmesine gerek olmadığını, kendisinin zaten pisuarı kullanırken pantolonunu indirdiğini ve herkesin onun poposunun nasıl göründüğünü bildiğini söyledim.

Tyson ve ben uzun süre müzik odasında kaldık ama sonunda kokumuzu almak için Justin Spitzer'i kullanan iki öğretmen bizi yakaladı.

Refakatçiler bizi diğer Üçüncü Takım üyelerinin de toplanmış olduğu kütüphaneye götürdüler.

İkinci kattaki kola makinesinin arkasında gizlendiğini bildiğim Christopher Brownfield dışında herkes oradaydı.

Tyson, Bay Tanner'a resimdekinin kendi kolu olduğunu söyledi. Neyse ki Tyson'ın dirseğinde resimdekine uyan bir ben var. Yoksa Bay Tanner'ın ona inanacağını sanmıyordum.

Bay Tanner, fotoğrafa ve Tyson'ın koluna birkaç kez daha baktıktan sonra, "masum bir hata" yaptığını ve "mantıklı" her insanın aynı şeyi yapacağını söyledi. Bu bana çok uyduruk bir özür gibi geldi ama en azından artık velilerimizi çağırmaktan söz etmediği için memnundum.

Sonra parti oyunları bitti. Yetişkinler uyku vaktinin geldiğini söylediler. Şamata'ya katılan herkesin bütün geceyi ayakta geçirmeyi planladığını sanıyorum. Ama bu noktada, eğer gece daha çabuk geçecekse, uyumaya çoktan razıydım.

Uyku tulumuma girmek için oditoryuma gittim. Benim uyku tulumum, pek de fena bir kız olmayan Jennifer Houseman'ın yanındaydı. Ama yetişkinler kızların eşyalarını alıp koridorun öbür ucundaki kütüphane medya salonuna taşımaları gerektiğini söylediler. Oğlanlar, oditoryumda kalmak zorundaydı.

Birazcık dinlenebileceğimi umuyordum ama bir sürü oğlan etrafta koşuşturmaya başladı. Bu durumda uyumak imkânsızdı.

Bir ara George Fleer insanları kovalamaya başladı. Çok korkunçtu.

Benim yaşımdaki oğlanların böyle şeyler yapmalarına hiç dayanamıyorum canım. Bazen bir sürü vahşi hayvana dönüyorlar.

Geroge milleti kovalamaya başlayınca, ben de dişlerimi fırçalamak için tuvalete kaçtım. Tuvalet, oditoryumun arka tarafında. Işıklar da kapalıydı. Bu yüzden o taraf zifiri karanlıktı.

Garip bir ses duydum ve bir an çok korktum.
Çünkü okulumuzun kemirgenlerle başı dertte.
Ama sonra sesin tek başına langırt oynayan
Fregley'den geldiğini anladım.

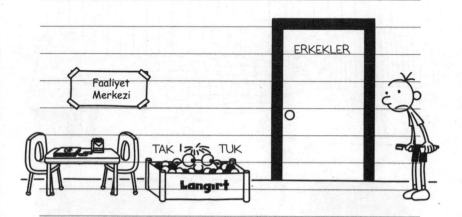

Gece yarısı civarı, okulun rehberlik danışmanı
Bay Palmero, herkese uyku tulumlarının
içine girip uyumalarını söyledi. Bütün gece
başka konuşma istemediğini, kimsenin cıt bile
çıkarmaması gerektiğini ekledi.

Biraz sonra biri gaz çıkardı. Bay Palmero deliye
döndü ama sesin kimden geldiğini anlayamadı.

Fotoğraflar konusunda yaşananlardan sonra, galiba yetişkinler popoyla ilgili her şey konusunda çok hassastılar.

Bay Palmero "içindeki gazı boşaltma" ihtiyacı duyan kişinin sahnedeki perdenin arkasına geçip bunu orada yapabileceğini söyledi.

Bundan sonra bir sürü oğlan sırayla Bay Palmero'ya perdenin arkasına geçmesi gerektiğini söylemeye başladı. Sonra da duyabileceğiniz en iğrenç sesleri çıkarmaya başladılar.

Bu bir süre devam etti. David Rosenburg müzik odasına gidip bir tubayla döndüğünde de zirveye ulaştı.

Tesadüf mü bilmiyorum ama tam o sırada oditoryumda hava buz gibi oldu.

Galiba biri klimayı açmıştı. Tek bildiğim, o dakikadan sonra kimse uyku tulumlarından çıkamadı.

Bir süre sonra Bay Palmero uyudu ama bütün oğlanlar uyanıktı. Bazıları buranın hapishaneden farksız olduğunu söylüyordu. Herkes firar edip eve dönmekten söz etmeye başlamıştı.

Sorun, bütün kapıların kilitlenmiş olmasıydı. Şamata bizim için felakete dönüşmüştü.

Albert Sandy, bir adamın hapisten kaşık kullanarak kaçtığı bir film izlediğini söyledi. Bu fikir bir sürü kişiyi çok heyecanlandırdı.

Ama sonra bunun bir Hollywood saçmalığı olduğu anlaşıldı. Çünkü mutfaktan kaşıklar getirdik ama muşamba zeminde bir delik bile açamadık.

Saat sabaha karşı bir buçukta, birisi dışarıdaki yanıp sönen ışıkları fark etti. Hepimiz neler olup bittiğini görmek için oditoryumun arka tarafında toplandık.

Çekici şirketinden gelen bir adam, Bay Palmero'nun yasak yere park edilmiş arabasının etrafında dolaşıyordu.

Bizi okuldan kurtarması için, adamın dikkatini çekmeye çalıştık.

Ama adam bizi duymadı ve Bay Palmero'nun
arabasını çekti. Önce Bay Palmero'yu uyandırıp
ona söylemeyi düşündüm ama sonra kendisini
rahat bırakmamız gerektiğine karar verdim.

Bu arada oditoryum o kadar soğuktu ki, vücut
ısımızı korumak için birbirimize iyice sokulduk.
Balık istifi gibiydi.

Kütüphane medya odası sıcak ve huzurlu
olmalıydı. Ciddi ciddi oraya gidip kızların arasına
karışmayı düşünüyordum.

Ama nasıl olsa beni yakalarlardı ve başladığım
yere geri dönerdim.

Saat iki buçuk civarında uyumuş olmalıyım.
Saat üçte kapı vuruldu ve herkes uyandı. Bay
Palmero kapıyı açtı. Dışarıda bir grup öfkeli veli
dikiliyordu.

Anlaşılan her şeyin yolunda olduğundan emin olmak için bütün gece çocuklarını aramışlardı. Ama çocuklar cevap vermiyordu çünkü Bay Tanner herkesin cep telefonlarını almıştı. Sonra veliler birbirlerini aramışlardı ve herkes paniğe kapılmıştı.

Uzun lafın kısası, okula gelen veliler çocuklarını alıp eve götürdüler. Geriye sadece cep telefonu olmayan iki çocuk kaldı: ben ve Rowley. Bu da çok fenaydı.

İçimden bir ses, bu Şamata fikrinin velilerle öğretmenlerin biz çocukları kızlı erkekli partilerden soğutmak için düzenlenen bir plan olduğunu söylüyor. Eğer bu doğruysa, işlem tamamdır!

Hafta sonunu Şamata'nın etkisinden kurtulmaya çalışarak geçirdim; çünkü cuma gecesi sıfır uyku uyumuştum. Ama sanırım bu deneyim bünyeme ağır geldi çünkü bu sabah uyandığımda hastaydım.

Daha önce okuldan kaçmak için hasta numarası yaptığımı itiraf ediyorum ama annem genellikle numaramı yutmuyor.

Ama bugün annem ateşimi ölçtü. Herhalde çok yüksekti çünkü annem yataktan çıkmamamın iyi olacağını söyledi.

Bugün kütüphanede akşam gireceği son sınavına çalışması gerektiğini, bu yüzden evde kalıp benimle ilgilenemeyeceğini ekledi. Bu çok fenaydı, çünkü hasta olmanın tek iyi tarafı, birinin size şefkat gösterip üzerinize düşmesidir.

Annem, Isabella'nın bugün çalışacağını ve eğer acil bir durum olursa ona gidebileceğimi söyledi. Ama annem çıkınca, odamın kapısını kilitledim çünkü ISabella'nın öğle uykusu için odama gelmesinden korkuyordum.

Öğlene doğru dalmış olmalıyım. Uyandığımda, alt katta kıyamet kopuyordu. Televizyonun sesi sonuna kadar açılmıştı; bir de bir sürü kadın konuşuyordu sanki.

Pencereden baktım ve evin önünde bir sürü araba olduğunu gördüm.

Neler olduğunu bilmiyordum, bu yüzden odamdan çıkmadım. Yarım saat kadar sonra, annem arabasıyla geldi ve eve girdi. Beş dakika sonra, Isabella da dahil olmak üzere bütün kadınlar dışarı akın ettiler.

Annem yukarı çıkıp odama geldi. Burnundan soluyordu.

Benimle ilgilenmek için kütüphaneden erken çıkıp eve gelmiş. Gelince de, mahalledeki bütün hizmetçilerin bizim evde pembe dizi partisi verdiğini görmüş.

ÖP BENİ, REX. ÖP BENİ DE HAFIZAM YERİNE GELSİN!

Annem bu gece bir ev toplantısı daha yaptı ve artık Isabella'nın hizmetlerine gerek kalmadığını, evle elbirliğiyle ilgileneceğimizi söyledi. Bunu duyduğuma sevindim çünkü artık yatağımda külotlu çorap aramaktan vazgeçebilirim.

Salı

Bugün okula gittiğimde, Rowley dolabımın yanında dikiliyordu ve yüzünde kocaman bir gülümseme vardı. Sonra alnında büyük bir sivilce olduğunu fark ettim.

Bir sürü insan, öyle bir sivilceyle okula bile gelmez. Ama Rowley dedi ki:

Bu nedense canımı sıktı. Ama hepsi bu kadar da değildi.

Daha sonra Rowley'yi büyük çocukların dolaplarının etrafında dolaşırken gördüm. Galiba sırf sivilcesi var diye, onu aralarına kabul edeceklerini filan sanıyor.

Rowley'nin insanları aptal bir sivilceyle etkilemeye çalışması bence çok acıklı!

İnanın bana, kıskandığım filan yok. Ama bu, her gece pofuduk hayvanlarıyla uyuyan bir çocuk. Bu yüzden sivilcesinin benden önce çıkması çok saçma!

177

Bu olay beni düşünmeye itti. Ben de boyumun uzamasını ya da en azından sakallarımın çıkmasını dört gözle bekliyorum ama her şey çok yavaş ilerliyor.

Ama şimdi Rowley'nin sivilcesi ve onun cephesinde bir şeyler daha çabuk olduğu için imreniyorum.

Bugün okuldan döndüğümde, bir şeyler değişmiş mi diye aynada kendime baktım. Ama her şey her zamankinden farksızdı.

Ben de yemekten sonra annemle babama ne zaman bir şeyler olacağını sordum.

Ama kendileri de benim yaşımdayken bu tür meseleler konusunda arkadaşlarından çok geride olduklarını söylediler.

Sonra babam, yetişkin olduğumda da sakallar konusunda çok şey beklememem gerektiğini, çünkü kendisinin kocaman adam olduğunu ama haftada bir ya da iki kez tıraş olmasının yettiğini söyledi.

ÇOK kötü haberlerdi bunlar. Bu ülkede hep büyüyüp ne isterseniz olabileceğiniz söyleniyor ama şimdi bunun doğru olmadığını fark ediyorum.

Eğer sakalım ya da bıyığım olmazsa,
yapamayacağım en az yarım düzine iş sayabilirim.

SİHİRBAZ   KORSAN   ORMANCI

RESSAM   POLİS   SUÇLU

Çarşamba

Bugün Rowley'nin sivilcesinin ikinci günüydü. O
da herkes sivilceyi daha iyi görsün diye saçlarını
perde gibi ortadan ikiye ayırmıştı.

Böyle bir gün daha geçirmeye dayanamazdım; bu konuda bir şeyler yapmaya karar verdim. Bir not yazdım ve koridorda Rowley'ye uzattım.

Sevgili Rowley,

Kimse senin sivilcenden hoşlanmıyor.

imza
Kızlar

Numaramın işe yaramasına çok sevindim.

Ama tam öğle tatilinden önce, çok acayip bir şey oldu. Bizim sınıf kantine gidiyordu. Koridorda büyük çocukların dolaplarının yanından geçerken, arkadaşlarıyla birlikte dikilen Jordan Jury'yi gördük.

Jordan bizi durdurdu ve dedi ki:

Buna inanamıyordum. Daha önce de dediğim gibi, Jordan Jury'nin partileri EFSANEDİR.

Ama Jordan'ın partilerinin en iyi tarafı KIZLARIN da olmasıdır. Yani onun partileri, benim genellikle davet edildiğim partilerden çok farklıdır.

Yani, burada GERÇEK bir partiden söz ediyoruz. Ortalığı bir milyon refakatçinin idare ettiği Şamata gibi bir şeyden değil.

Jordan Jury'nin beni ve Rowley'yi bu partiye neden davet ettiği konusunda hiçbir fikrim yok. Benim matematik kitabım yüzünden, Rowley'nin sivilcesi yüzünden ya da her ikisi yüzünden olabilir.

Ama kesin olan bir şey var. Jordan bizim Rowley ile arkadaş olduğumuzu düşündü ve ikimizi birlikte davet etti.

Ben de onun fikrini değiştirmesine neden olacak bir şey yapmak istemedim.

Benden büyük sınıflardaki kızlarla "Şişe Çevirmece" oynayabileceksem, bir gece Rowley ile arkadaşmışım gibi davranmaya çoktan razıyım!

<u>Perşembe</u>
Buna inanamayacaksınız ama annem Jordan'ın partisine gitmeme izin vermiyor.

Üstelik bunun sebebi kızlı-erkekli olması değil. Büyük çocukların gelecek olması da değil. Neymiş efendim, hafta sonu Gary Amca'nın düğünü varmış.

Kötü zamanlama konusunda bu bir dünya rekoru olmalı. Anneme benim evde kalmama ve partiye gitmeme izin vermesi için yalvardım ama annem ikna olmadı. Üstelik Gary Amca'nın bir sonraki düğününe gideceğime dair söz verdiğim halde!

Annem bunu kaçıramayacağımı, gitmezsem Gary Amca'nın moralinin çok bozulacağını söyledi.

İyi de ben Gary Amca'nın bütün düğünlerine gittim. Neler olacağını size kelimesi kelimesine anlatabilirim.

Gary Amca, benden "okuyucu" olmamı isteyecek. Yetişkinler düğünlerde hep Kutsal Kitap'tan bölümler okuması için bir çocuğu seçiyorlar. Çünkü herkes bir çocuğun isimleri telaffuz edememesinin çok şeker olduğunu düşünüyor.

Annemin fikrini değiştirmeyeceğini biliyordum, ben de mücadele ederek vakit kaybetmedim. Odama gidip Rowley'yi aradım.

Rowley'ye ben partiye gidemediğime göre kendisinin de gidemeyeceğini söyledim. Ben amcamın düğününde tıkılıp kalmışken onun gitmesinin haksızlık olacağını açıkladım.

Ama Rowley artık bir yetişkin olduğunu, KENDİ kararlarını verebileceğini, bu yüzden de ne olursa olsun partiye gideceğini söyledi.

O kadar kızdım ki telefonu suratına kapattım. Şimdi Rowley hakkında ne demek istediğimi anladınız mı? Bu bencil hareket, artık onunla arkadaş olmadığımız için sevinmemi sağladı.

Cumartesi
Dün bizim aile arabaya doluştu ve Gary Amca'nın düğünü için Gammie'nin evine gittik. Parti meselesi yüzünden ben çok keyifsizdim. Ayrıca başka bir şey daha vardı.

Gammie ile "Konuşma"nın bu hafta sonu olacağını hatırlamıştım ve kesinlikle bir söylev dinleyecek havada değildim.

Son söylevi babamın ağabeyi Jim Amca'dan dinlemiştim. Bana artık ortaokulda olduğuma göre "geleceğim" hakkında düşünmeye başlamam gerektiğini söylemişti.

Jim Amca bir şema çizdi ve bana bugünden itibaren liseye kadar, iyi bir üniversiteye gitmek ve sonrasında iyi bir iş bulmak için yapmam gereken her şeyi gösterdi. Görünüşe göre babam ve Jim Amca hayatımın gelecek on yılını planlamışlardı

Her neyse, ben bunları düşünüyordum. O sırada bir şey oldu ve beni sıkıntılı ruh halimden kurtardı.

Annem Gammie'yi arayıp biraz geç kalacağımızı, yolda smokinimi almak için durmamız gerektiğini söyledi.

İşte bu ilgimi çekti. Gary Amca'nın daha önceki düğünlerinden hiçbirinde smokin giymem gerekmemişti. Bu bir tek anlama gelebilirdi. SAĞDIÇLARDAN biri ben olacağım.

Düğünden önceki gece sağdıçlar damat şerefine acayip bir parti veriyorlar. Böyle bir partiye katılmayı çok isteyecek kadar kablolu TV izledim.

Rodrick adına biraz üzüldüm aslında çünkü bu onu atladıkları anlamına geliyordu. Neyse, ben de partide fotoğraflar çeker, onun göremeyeceği her şeyi görmesini sağlarım napalım.

Ama öte yandan çok mutluyum çünkü Rowley ortaokulda uyduruk bir partideyken, ben limuzine binecek ve hayatımın en güzel zamanlarını geçireceğim. Bu hafta sonundan sonra "erkek" kimmiş göreceğiz.

Bir de bonus olarak, düğünde nedimelerden biriyle eşleşeceğim. Sonja'nın tatlı arkadaşları olsun diye dua ediyorum.

Gammie'nin evine doğru giderken yolda annem bana akrabaların öpücüklerini silmeyeceğime dair söz verdirdi, çünkü bu "kabalıkmış".

Ama elimde değil. Teyzelerden ya da kuzinlerden biri beni yanağımdan ıslak ıslak öptüğünde orada çoğalan bakterileri düşünmeye başlıyorum ve kaşınıyorum. Gammie'nin evine son gittiğimizde, bu sorunu çözmek için yanımda antibakteriyel ıslak mendillerden götürdüm.

Ama anneme bu kez öpücükleri silmeyeceğime dair söz verdim. Bunu yapmamalıymışım çünkü bizi her defasında beni dudaklarımdan öpen Dorothy Teyze karşıladı.

Annemin görüş alanından çıkar çıkmaz gidip bulabildiğim ilk şeyle yüzümü sildim.

Biz Gammie'nin evine vardığımızda, ailenin çoğu gelmişti. Herkesi, teker teker saymaya ömrüm yetmez. Bu yüzden bazılarını anlatayım.

Kuzenim Benjy anne babası, Patricia Teyze ve Tony Enişte ile oradaydı. Benjy'yi son gördüğümde sadece iki kelime söyleyebiliyordu:

Babamın kuzeni Terrence de oradaydı. Ondan söz etmemin tek nedeni, herkesin beni onun küçüklüğüne benzetmesi. Bu da çok sinir bozucu.

Bunu ilk duyduğumda, doğru olup olmadığını görmek için Gammie'nin fotoğraf albümüne bakmıştım. Ne yazık ki doğruydu.

Bu yüzden sanırım estetik ameliyat için şimdiden para biriktirmeye başlasam iyi olacak.

Babamın kuzeni Byron da oradaydı. Onu gördüğüme de pek sevinmedim. Son aile toplantısında, Gammie Byron'u süt almaya göndermişti, ben de onunla gitmiştim. Ama evden çıktıktan bir kilometre sonra, çukura girmişti ve lastik patlamıştı.

Byron bana eve gidip yardım çağırmamı söyledi. Yolda yağmur başladı. Kapıdan içeri girdiğinde, mutfaktaki kadınların hepsi yerleri çamurladım diye bana bağırdı.

196

Ayakkabılarımı çıkarıp antrede bırakmamı söylediler, ben de öyle yaptım. Ama bağırışlar yüzünden sersemlemiş olmalıyım ki Byron'ın patlayan lastiğini tamamen unuttum. Byron yarım saat sonra geldiğinde, pek de mutlu görünmüyordu.

Charlie Amca da gelmişti. Onu gördüğüme gerçekten çok sevindim çünkü onun cepleri hep biz çocuklar için aldığı şekerlerle dolu oluyor.

197

Ama eskiden Charlie Amca'yı sevmezdim çünkü benimle dalga geçerdi. O zamanlar kırmızı komik pijamalarım vardı. Charlie Amca da beni her gördüğünde aynı şeyi söylerdi:

Bu nedense içime dokunmuş. Anneme hissettiklerimi anlattım. O da beni yeni pijamalar almak için mağazaya götürdü. Bu kez mavi pijamalar aldı. Bir dahaki sefere Charlie Amca'yı gördüğümde, onu alt ettiğimi biliyordum.

Ama bana YENİ bir lakap takması ancak birkaç saniye sürdü.

Gammie'nin evine gelmeyen tek kişi Lawrence Amca'ydı. Ama bu da büyük bir sürpriz değildi. Lawrence Amca sürekli seyahat ediyor ve aile toplantılarına hemen hiç gelmiyor. Ancak bazen webcam ile katılıyor. Büyük Büyükbaba Chester'ın cenazesinde öyle yapmıştı mesela.

En son gelenler Gary Amca ve nişanlısı Sonja oldu. Sonja gayet hoş görünüyordu. Davranışlarına bakılacak olsa birbirlerine deli oluyor gibiler.

Ne yazık ki yemekte onların yanına oturmak zorunda kaldım ve bunu kendi gözlerimle gördüm.

Babam yolda bize, Sonja'nın Gary Amca'nın daha önce evlenmiş olması konusunda hassas olduğunu, bu yüzden bu konuyu açmamamız gerektiğini söylemişti.

Meğer Sonja, Gary Amca'ya sol kolundaki dövmeyi sildirmesini söylemiş çünkü dövmede Gary Amca'nın ilk karısının adı yazıyordu.

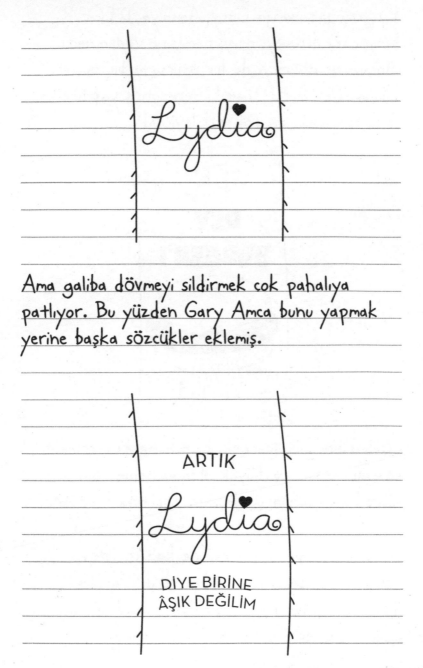

Lydia ♥

Ama galiba dövmeyi sildirmek çok pahalıya patlıyor. Bu yüzden Gary Amca bunu yapmak yerine başka sözcükler eklemiş.

ARTIK

Lydia ♥

DİYE BİRİNE
ÂŞIK DEĞİLİM

En azından Sonja Gary Amca'ya DIĞER kolundaki dövmeyi değiştirmesini söylememiş. Amcam bu dövmeyi de bir oturuşta bir buçuk kiloluk Dev Burger'i yedikten sonra yaptırmıştı. İtiraf etmeliyim, çok etkileyiciydi.

DEV BURGER'i YEDİM

Söylediğim gibi, ailedeki hemen herkes gelmişti ve Gammie'nin evi büyük olduğu halde, bazı kişiler aynı odayı paylaşmak zorunda kaldılar.

Ne zaman Gammie'nin evinde kalsak, ben Gammie'nin "Bekârlar" adını verdiği gruba düşüyorum. Bu grup, adından da anlaşılacağı gibi, hiç evlenmemiş erkeklerden oluşuyor.

BEKÂRLAR

Bu, benim birlikte kalmaya pek hevesli olduğum bir grup değil. ÖZELLİKLE Gammie'nin konuk odasında sadece iki yatak olduğu için. BU da kimimizin ayak uçlu yatması, bazılarının da yerde yatmak zorunda kalması anlamına geliyor.

OF, AYAKLARIN BUZ GİBİ!

John Amca da bekârlardan biriydi ama geçen baharda evlendi. Acaba böyle durumlarda bizimle yatmak zorunda kalmamak için mi evlendi diye düşünmeye başladım.

Aynı odanın içinde bir sürü insan horlarken uyumak çok zordu. Ben de toparlandım ve kendime geceyi geçirecek bir yer aramaya başladım.

Bulabildiğim tek yer, Gammie'nin odasının yanındaki banyoydu. Ben de battaniyemi ve yastığımı küvete koydum ve kendime yatak yaptım. Rahat değildi ama en azından kendi başıma kalabilecektim.

Neyse ki bu sabah Gammie banyo yapmak için geldiğinde, tam zamanında uyandım.

Ucuz atlattığım bu felaketten sonra, bütün günü ayakta geçirdim. Çok uzun bir gün oldu çünkü prova yemeği saat tam yedideydi.

Ama en azından, daha sonra sağdıçlarla nefis bir partiye katılacağımı biliyordum.

Böyle aile toplantılarının sorunu, çocukları düşünmemeleri. Bu yüzden eğer çay içmiyor ve kadınlarla dedikodu yapmıyorsan, şansına küs.

Gammie'nin evindeki her şey de yaşlı insanlar içindi. Bir çocuğun kendini oyalayabileceği hiçbir şey yoktu. Birkaç yıl önce anneme bu konuda yakınmıştım; o da Gammie'nin evinde kalması için Legolar satın almıştı. Ama Gammie küçücük parçaların evin her tarafına yayılmasından hoşlanmadığından, bunları kocaman bir blok halinde birbirine yapıştırmış.

Üstelik Gammie'nin evinde bir çocuğun hoşuna gidebilecek hiçbir şey de yok. Şöminenin üzerindeki kavanozda sert şekerler var, TAMAM. Geçen yıl bunlardan birkaç tane yemiştim. Ama tatları berbattı. Bir de şekerler sakız gibiydi, çok zor çiğneniyordu.

Sonunda midem bulanmıştı ve birkaç saat kanepede yatmak zorunda kalmıştım.

Meğer kavanozdaki şekerler çok BAYATMIŞ!

Babam KENDİ çocukluğunda da orada şekerler olduğunu söyledi. Hatta bunu kanıtlamak için Gammie'nin albümünden bir fotoğraf buldu.

Küçük Frankie şekerlerin tadını çıkarıyor

Fotoğraflardan söz etmişken, Gammie'nin şöminenin üzerindeki fotoğrafları güncellemesi gerek artık. Ailedeki herkesin fotoğrafları var. Rodrick ile benim de yaklaşık sekiz yıl önce Santa'nın Köyü'ne gittiğimizde çekilmiş fotoğrafımız duruyor.

Kimsenin bakmadığı bir sırada o resmi kaldırıp atmak istiyorum. Çünkü ünlü olduğumda biyografim yayınlandığında, bu resmi de mutlaka ortaya çıkarırlar.

Noel Hatırası

Gammie'nin evindeki bütün mobilyalar eski ve belli ki değerli. Gammie öldüğünde bu eşyalardan kime ne kalacağı konusunda büyük bir kavga çıkacağından eminim. Hatta insanlar şimdiden mobilyaların üzerine üstünde isimlerinin yazdığı çıkartmalar yapıştırmaya başladılar bile.

Ben bunun Gammie'ye büyük bir saygısızlık olduğunu düşünüyorum. Ama benim de kendime almak istediğim bir iki eşya olduğunu itiraf etmeliyim.

Pazar

Dün akşam prova yemeği boyunca, Gary Amca'nın beni yanına çağırmasını ve bekârlığa veda partisinin nerede olacağını söylemesini bekledim. Ama böyle bir şey olmadı.

Ben de düğün programına baktım ve adımı en altta gördüm.

Yüzük Taşıyıcı / Çiçek Çocuk	Manny Heffley
Yardımcı Çiçek Çocuk	Greg Heffley
Lütfen kilisede flaşlı fotoğraf çekmeyin.	

Bundan kurtulmaya ve yardımcı çiçek çocuk görevlerimi Benjy'ye devretmeye çalıştım. Ama annem bu yıl Benjy'nin okuyucu olacağını, üstelik Manny ile benim bir örnek beyaz smokinlerimizin olduğunu söyledi.

Yani Rowley, Jordan Jury'nin partisinde çılgınlar gibi eğlenirken, ben Manny için bir sepet dolusu gül yaprağı tutuyordum. Rodrick'in de bol bol fotoğraf çektiğini gördüm. Bunları şimdiye kadar internete yüklemediyse çok şaşarım.

Düğün töreninden sonra, yemeklerin servis edildiği salona geçtik.

Ama biz yemeğe başlamadan önce, Gary Amca'nın baş sağdıcı Leonard ayağa kalktı ve kadeh kaldırdı.

Leonard, Gary Amca ile Sonja'nın flört ettikleri günlere dair çok komik bir hikâyesi olduğunu, bunu herkesle paylaşmak istediğini söyledi. İki ay önce, Gary Amca Sonja'yı beysbol maçına götürmüş. Ondan ayrılmayı planlıyormuş çünkü onun yerine kız kardeşiyle flört etmeye başlamak niyetindeymiş.

Ama Gary Amca, Sonja ile ayrılık konuşmasını yapamadan, gökyüzünde kuyruğunda bir pankart asılı bir uçak belirmiş.

Leonard, stadyumda Sonja adında kız arkadaşı olan bir adamın daha olması gerektiğini söyledi. Ama Gary Amca'nın Sonja'sı, onun bir şey söylemesine fırsat kalmadan tepkisini göstermiş.

Gary Amca bunun bir yanlış anlaşılma olduğunu açıklamaya çalışmış ama Sonja'yı üzerse etraflarındaki erkeklerin kendisini dövmelerinden korkmuş. Bu yüzden idare etmeye karar vermiş. Önce Leonard'ın hikâyesinin sadece bir şaka olduğunu düşündüm ama Gary Amca iskemlesinden fırlayıp bunun doğru olmadığını söylemedi.

Her neyse, içimden bir ses gelecek yıl Gary Amca'nın BEŞİNCİ düğününe gideceğimizi söylüyor.

Kokteylden sonra hepimiz üzerimizi değiştirmek için Gammie'nin evine gittik. Babam odaya girip Gammie'nin benimle konuşmak istediğini söylediğinde, eşyalarımı topluyordum. Önce Gammie'nin benimle neden özel konuşmak istediğini anlamadım. Sonra "Konuşma" vaktinin geldiğini fark ettim.

Koridoru geçip Gammie'nin odasına giderken, biraz gergindim. Ama aynı zamanda heyecanlıydım da. Gammie bizim gittiğimiz yollardan en az on kez gidip gelmiş bir kadın, bu yüzden epey bilgelik depolamış olmalıydı. Doğrusunu söylemem gerekirse, ben de bunun birazını kullanabileceğimi düşünüyordum.

İçeri girip kapıyı arkamdan kapattım. Gammie şık bir koltukta oturuyordu. O onun karşısına geçtim. Ben oturunca, Gammie hemen konuşmaya başladı.

Gammie, benim yaşımdaki çocukların çoğunun büyümek için acele ettiğini, oysa birazcık aklım varsa, yaşadıklarımın tadını çıkarmam gerektiğini söyledi.

Aynı sözleri annemle babamdan da milyonlarca kez duymuştum. O yüzden konuşmanın gidişatı beni hayal kırıklığına uğratmıştı.

Ama Gammie'nin sözleri bitmemişti daha. Benim "Tipsizlik Yılları"na girmeye hazırlandığımı, dudaklarımın kalınlaşacağını, cildimin bozulacağını, liseye başlayana kadar kafamın bedenime göre çok büyük görüneceğini söyledi.

Sonra önümüzdeki birkaç yıl içinde kimsenin resmimi çekmesine izin vermemem gerektiğini, eğer bunu yaparsam pişman olacağımı ekledi. Aynı öğüdü babama, Gary Amca'ya ve Joe Amca'ya da vermiş ama onlar dinlememişler.

GARY AMCA   JOE AMCA   BABA

Gammie'nin sözleri hâlâ bitmemişti. Bana yaşlanmanın hiç kolay bir şey olmadığını, onun yaşına gelmenin ÇOK FENA olduğunu söyledi.

Sonra "hemoroidler"den, "zona"dan ve daha önce hiç duymadığım başka şeylerden söz etmeye başladı. Kafamın karıştığını anlamış olmalı ki çorabını indirdi ve bana neden söz ettiğini gösterdi.

KIVIR
KIVIR

İşte o anda izin isteyip odadan kaçtım. İyi ki Gammie başka giysilerini de çıkarmaya karar vermeden önce oradan uzaklaşmışım.

Yarım saat sonra eşyalarımızı topladık, arabaya bindik ve eve doğru yola koyulduk. Hafta sonu sona erdiği için mutluydum. Akrabalarımı seviyorum, tamam ama sürekli onlarla iç içe olmaya dayanamıyorum.

HEY! BURADA ÇİŞLİ BEZ VAR!

Pazartesi

Bugün okula dönmek işkence gibiydi. Çünkü görünüşe göre herkes Jordan Jury'nin partisine gitmişti ve tabi herkes bunu konuşmak istiyordu.

Büyük çocukların koridorundan geçmek en fenasıydı.

Aslında gitmediğime memnun oldum. Çünkü Jordan'ın benim sınıfımdaki çocukları davet etmesinin nedeni bizi uşak olarak kullanmak istemesiymiş.

Bu akşam haberlerde Tatlı Meltem Çocuğu yarışmasını kazananı açıkladılar. Ne yazık ki ben seçilmemişim. Ama SEÇİLEN çocuğu tanıyorum.

Bizim sokağın biraz aşağısında oturan Scotty Douglas adındaki çocuk seçilmiş. Onu neden seçtiler hiç anlamadım, çünkü seçmelerde sloganı bile doğru dürüst söyleyemiyordu.

Ama Tatlı Meltem'deki insanlar araştırmış olmalılar, çünkü eğer Scotty'nin ağabeyini görseler iki kez düşünmeleri gerekirdi.

Dün gece annem ilk yarıyıl bittiğine göre akademik kariyerini bir süre "askıya alacağını" ve ailesiyle daha çok zaman geçireceğini söyledi. Bunu duyduğuma ne kadar sevindiğimi anlatamam. Galiba işler sonunda normale dönüyor.

Aslında bu yıl sorun buydu. Birdenbire bir sürü şey değişti ve ben her şeyin ESKİ halinden memnundum.

Babam ve Joe Amca gibi kişiler benim sorumluluklarımı bilmem ve geleceğimi ciddi ciddi düşünmeye başlamam gerektiğini söyleyip duruyorlar. Ama aslında ben daha çok Gary Amca'ya benzediğimi düşünüyorum.

Sanırım artık büyümek için acele etmiyorum. Gammie bana gelecek birkaç yıl içinde başıma gelecekleri gösterdikten sonra, galiba onun öğüdünü tutacağım ve büyümeyi olabildiğince geciktireceğim.

Salı

İşlerin normale dönmesinden söz etmişken, Rowley ile benim de son iki ayı geride bırakmamız ve arkadaşlığımıza devam etmemiz gerektiğine karar verdim.

Onunla uzun bir geçmişimiz var. Saçma sapan bir şey yüzünden bunu yok saymak anlamsız.

Doğrusunu söylemem gerekirse, neden kavga ettiğimizi bile hatırlamıyorum.

Bugün okuldan sonra, Rowley'ye dışarıda bir şeyler yapmak isteyip istemediğini sormak için onun evine gittim. Beni görünce o kadar sevindi ki utandım.

Rowley bana sonsuza dek "sıkı dost" olup olmayacağımızı sordu. Sonra bana her zaman takmam için ısrar ettiği sevgi kolyesinin yarısını verdi.

Ona kolyeyi takmayacağımı çünkü kızlara göre olduğunu söyledim. Ama doğrusu şu "sonsuza dek" ifadesi beni geriyor. Ona belki bir aylık dilimler belirlememizin daha iyi olacağını söyledim. Hemen razı oldu.

Ama bir şey söyleyeceğim. Rowley yazdan beri birkaç santim uzamış. Bu çocuk ne kadar uzun boylu olacak KİM BİLİR!

En azından liseye başlayana kadar onunla takılsam iyi olacak galiba. Çünkü eğer bu hızla büyümeye devam ederse, Rowley'nin yanımda olması benim yararıma.

TEŞEKKÜRLER

Bu hikâyeleri yazmam konusunda bana ilham veren ve motivasyon sağlayan tüm Saftirik dizisi hayranlarına teşekkürler. Kitaplarımın çocuklara ulaşmasını sağlayan tüm dünyadaki kitapçılara teşekkürler.

Sevgi ve destekleri için aileme teşekkürler. Bu deneyimi sizinle paylaşmak çok keyifli.

Bu kitabın ortaya çıkması için ellerinden geleni fazlasıyla yapan Abrams çalışanlarına teşekkürler. Editörüm Charlie Kochman'a, danışmanım Jason Wells'e ve yayın yönetmenim Scott Auerbach'a özellikle teşekkür ediyorum.

Greg Heffley'ye hayat vermek için çok çalışan Hollywood'daki herkese, özellikle Nina, Brad, Carla, Riley, Elizabeth ve Thor'a teşekkür ederim. Sylvie ve Keith, yardımlarınız ve rehberliğiniz için teşekkürler.

YAZAR HAKKINDA

Jeff Kinney online oyun geliştirmeci ve bir New York Times çok satan yazarıdır. 2009'da, Jeff, Time dergisi tarafından Dünyanın En Etkili 100 Kişisi'nden biri seçildi. Çocukluğu Washington D.C.'de geçen yazar 1995 yılında New England'a taşındı. Halen güney Massachusettes'te eşi ve iki oğluyla birlikte yaşıyor.

divisions, they continued to bubble to the surface, despite the strict controls the government was theoretically able to exert over industrial unrest in wartime. The days lost to strikes increased throughout 1942, 1943 and 1944. While the numbers fell somewhat in 1945, they were still at twice the 1939 level.

In part, this illustrates the strong position organised labour found itself in during the war, with government and employers both preferring to concede wage demands rather than lose war production. Bevin in particular saw a relatively light touch with industrial disputes as being part of the price he was willing to pay for the Draconian controls he exerted over other areas of industrial life.

Colonel Blimp explains: 'Gad sir, Henry Ford was right! Trades unionism is just a plot by the workers to stop employers treating them well of their own free will.'

Class resentment is illustrated by a Home Intelligence report of August/ September 1941:

There is 'considerable resentment among women who are already working that the middle and upper classes are still being allowed to "get away" with voluntary war jobs, as drivers, helpers in canteens, etc.' which can be made to look like whole-time work – 'but if such women want time off, there is never any difficulty with their getting it'. (This is contrasted with the great difficulty experienced by women factory workers in doing their household shopping. This problem is causing 'more and more discontent' and is thought to be 'seriously holding up the supply of woman-power'. Trades union representatives again complain that 'very few factories are giving facilities for shopping to their women workers'). The opinion appears to be general that compulsion is most needed 'among the women in the income groups in which the wage earner is receiving from £400 upwards'.

But, for some, the class-ridden British way of doing things was by divine appointment. Lieutenant-Colonel R.C. Bingham provoked a lively correspondence in *The Times* in January 1941 with the following:

Never was the old school tie and the best that it stands for more justified than it is today. Our new armies are being officered by classes of society who are new to the job. The middle, lower-middle and working classes are now receiving the King's Commission. These classes, unlike the old aristocratic and feudal (almost) classes who led the old army, have never had 'their people' to consider. They have never had anyone to think of but themselves. This aspect of life is completely new to them, and they have largely fallen down on it in their capacity as army officers.

. . . Man management is not a subject which can be 'taught'; it is an attitude of mind, and with the old school tie men this was instinctive and part of the philosophy of life.

If public schoolboys had the divine right to become officers, the ladies of the same class even had their own branch of the Armed Forces. The Voluntary Aid Detachments (VADs) consisted of some four thousand middle- and upper-class women who volunteered to do basic nursing and other duties for the Armed Forces. This gave them exemption from less desirable war work, such as munitions manufacturing. Proposals in 1942 to merge them with the predominantly working-class Auxiliary Territorial Service (ATS) led to a storm of protest – what one observer referred to as a 'monsoon in Mayfair' – in which a host of influential people were mobilised against the merger. Mary Stocks, a Labour Party supporter, lobbied Clement Attlee on the subject:

> The present VAD agitation is a social ramp boiled up by a few influential people on behalf of the wives and daughters of their friends. The VADs themselves ought to be ashamed to make such a fuss about the precise terms on which they will serve their country in wartime. I do hope someone will say this good and hard if the government allows a parliamentary discussion.

The armed forces were generally bastions of class prejudice. In the army, public school alumni were fourteen times more likely than their state-educated counterparts to be officers. In the Air Force, pilots of the officer caste were awarded the Distinguished Flying Cross for valour and got first-class rail travel. Equally brave Sergeant Pilots had to settle for the Distinguished Flying Medal and the third-class carriage. The Navy reserved half the places in its officer cadet scheme for public schoolboys. As First Lord of the Admiralty, Churchill had intervened in their selection process, personally interviewing three youths who had come in the top twenty of three hundred applicants, but had been rejected as 'unfit for naval service'. He found that two were the sons of non-commissioned sailors, while the third had rendered himself ineligible by possessing a slight cockney accent. Churchill got them admitted but, as soon as he was safely moved upstairs as prime minister, the Admiralty reverted to its pre-1913 policy of restricting 'lower deck' promotions.

Colonel Blimp explains: 'Gad sir, *The Times* is right! Fine sort of democracy this is, where young gentlemen of the Officer Training Corps haven't the right to be officers without serving in the ranks. Class distinction, that's what it is.'

Mass Observation visited the industries of the north in 1942 and found that pre-war attitudes of class struggle survived, undiluted by the war:

The most striking feature of the industrial scene here is the survival of strictly peacetime procedure in the conflict between employers and men, which is still today the predominant conflict here. One looked or listened in vain for any sign of a unity binding all parties in the fight against Germany. From the men, one got the fight against the management. From the management, one experienced hours of vituperation against the men. Both sides claimed to be only concerned with improving the situation to increase the strength of the struggle against fascism, but nevertheless, the real war which is being fought here today is still pre-war, private and economic.

Home Intelligence had found similar problems the previous year on a visit to Merseyside:

The workers' idea (possibly distorted) of the employers' attitude to the war effort appears important. It seems their patriotism is overshadowed by their unwillingness to make profits for the employers whom they regard as their natural enemies. Propaganda impressing workers of their importance, rather than encouraging their war effort, appears merely to incite them to use their increased bargaining power, whilst the recent publicity given to slacking in factories is regarded as an organised attempt by capitalists to throw the blame on workers to cover their own shortcomings. Keen workers with too little to do are said to be suffering from a sense of frustration which is leading to the feeling 'What's the use?'

Efforts to drive up productivity sometimes met with resistance, and the two sides of industry each had its own explanation for the problem. The President of the Board of Trade, writing to the prime minister in June 1941, had no doubt that the solution was for Churchill to tell the workers to pull their socks up:

> Colonel Blimp explains: 'Gad sir, Lord Nuts is right! The working class should be ashamed to ask for shorter hours, when the upper class is slaving themselves to the bone at dinners and balls.'

For some time I have heard from various industrialists with whom I am in touch stories that the workers in various vital industries are no longer putting forward their best efforts, and that there is an increasing slackness becoming apparent. In the last week or two such statements have become more numerous and are now coming to me from men in whose judgements I rely, and I therefore feel obliged to pass on this information.

The remedy suggested is always the same, namely that you should make a personal broadcast to the labour employed in vital industries, urging them to put forward an effort comparable to what they did last year.

But a *Daily Mirror* reporter, smuggled into the Vickers shipyard in Barrow in July 1940, found a very different picture, and came back with an indictment of management so damning that it could not be printed in its entirety at the time. It was recalled in Cecil King's war diary, *With Malice Towards None*:

> Seventy five per cent of the workforce he saw were doing nothing at all. Many had done no work for weeks and some not even for months, and all the men were completely fed up. There was ample material, willing and skilled men and quantities of machinery, but practically no output. One gun, which had been completed, was out in the rain and had been out for at least two months. Fourteen men he found asleep in a pocket in a big gun mounting.

Similar mismanagement was reported by a Liverpool girl, and quoted by Grafton:

> I went to work for Rootes, in their aircraft factory. I think they were making De Havilland Mosquitos. To be quite truthful I don't remember doing anything there. The hardest job I had was hiding away from the bosses. I was paid for nothing. I can picture to this day sitting under one of those aeroplanes.

The Minister of Labour, Ernest Bevin, thought one of the problems was that the workforce was hungry:

> It seems to be a case of one person telling another until they have made each other believe it. That there is a lethargy mainly due to physical conditions is true. We have run the food supply too low for the people on these heavy metal industries; their energy has been sapped and no appeals can make up for it.

The pressures of the war certainly took their toll of the labour force. The Ministry of Health Annual Report for 1942/3 spoke of complaints from around the country of a general increase in minor illness – reports of crowded surgeries and out-patients, more absenteeism and more complaints of feeling fatigued or 'run-down'. Sickness benefit claims were running above pre-war averages, even despite the absence of those workers now serving in the armed forces. A sample survey showed that 37 per cent of respondents thought their health worse than before the war and only 10 per cent thought it was better. Diet was blamed, and 10 per cent of the population was at that time classified as being malnourished or worse, but the pressures of long working hours and the other demands of war work were also beginning to tell on the labour force.

> The 'low state of health' of many people is commented on. . . . The wartime diet is regarded as the main cause; and to this are ascribed skin troubles, 'flu with bronchial or pneumonic symptoms, and the inability of people to throw off chills.
> Complaints of physical and nervous fatigue have been reported frequently during the past month. Absenteeism and industrial unrest are attributed partly to

the strain of long working hours combined with extra Civil Defence and household duties. Many feel the need of a 'real holiday' – women workers who are 'carrying on a double job' are particularly mentioned.

But Bevin seemed to come to the conclusion that under-achievement was partly a result of the labour force not feeling stressed enough. What they needed was rather more of a threat of invasion!

All the reports show that there is no defeatism and very little evidence of war weariness. Hard work, alterations in mode of life and various inconveniences are accepted as a necessary part of the war effort. . . .

But in the absence of military operations close to the country there is no fiery enthusiasm or sense of urgency among war workers collectively. . . . The possibility of defeat has not entered the heads of most workers, with the result that they are carrying on quietly, rather than urgently, more interested and concerned with their personal interests, their pay packets, their trade union activities, politics after the war, their food and minor comforts. They are anxious for victory but do not see the war as a major issue in their individual lives. There is not sufficient consciousness of their personal responsibility for achieving victory and of the need therefore to sacrifice their personal interests.

The long hours seen in industry were not reflected in government circles. As Neville Chamberlain's Private Secretary, John Colville was appalled to find that the staff at 10 Downing Street started work at 'the disgustingly early hour of 9.30 a.m.' Hugh Dalton had to issue instructions that his

---

MELT-DOWN

'Last week, the railings around Alexandra Park, Manchester, were taken down to the munitions melting pot. Last night, the watchman walked his three mile beat round the park with a bunch of keys, locking the six heavy iron gates. He will lock the gates every night until he receives orders to stop.'

Daily Express, 20 June 1940.

Others did not even keep their gates. Earl Baldwin, the former Prime Minister Stanley Baldwin, had the ornamental gates to his home requisitioned for the war effort by his pre-war foe, Lord Beaverbrook. They had been presented to him by a grateful electorate. This was a particularly vicious piece of revenge for long-remembered slights. Baldwin tried to appeal to Parliament to keep them, and a fellow Conservative MP gleefully told the House that he needed them 'to protect him from the just indignation of the mob'.

staff at the Ministry of Economic Warfare should be at their desks by 10.00 a.m., and until November 1940 the Foreign Office did not start until 11.00 a.m. Key government and senior military staff took extended leave, regardless of imminent threats of invasion or major military initiatives.

FOOD AND PRIVILEGE

While the very poorest in society were generally better nourished during the war years, for most people the wartime diet was probably more dispiriting than actually unhealthy. Home Intelligence reports from the middle years of the war none the less point to public concerns about the wartime diet and its effects upon productivity.

> People are inclined to blame 'vitamin deficiency in the wartime diet' for the prevalence of skin troubles, indigestion, colds and general debility, and to feel some resentment of official statements that 'The health of the nation is better than before the war.'

The shortage and lack of variety of food was a preoccupation throughout the war, and one's ability to overcome those shortages was one of the clearest divisions between the classes. As the war started, the introduction of rationing was seen by some as a measure that would balance out some of the grosser inequalities. Others, including Winston Churchill and a number of MPs from both major parties, felt that the image of 'starving Britain' that rationing would convey gave a propaganda coup to the Germans. The *Daily Express* ran a vigorous campaign against rationing:

> The public should revolt against the food rationing system, that dreadful and terrible iniquity which some of the Ministers want to adopt. There is no necessity for the trouble and expense of rationing because there may be a shortage of this or that inessential commodity. Why should old women be forced to wait here and there before the shops for their supplies? This form of folly is difficult and almost impossible to understand.

However, the experience of this East End grocer in the autumn of 1939 illustrates just how gross the inequalities of a free market could be:

> It is bringing all the rich people in from the West End to take the poor people's food. I came back from lunch this morning and found a beautiful car outside. A lady and her husband were carrying 28 pounds [of sugar] each – and the chauffeur was carrying 28 pounds on each arm. I made them put it all back again and gave them 3 pounds each. I don't think that sort of thing is right – they take the poor people's food. They don't give the poor people a chance.

Before state rationing was introduced, not all shopkeepers were prepared, like this man, to operate their own, informal system. There were plenty who were happy to put their prices up and sell to whoever could afford it, in whatever quantities they wanted to buy. Others gave preferential service to favoured customers, saving goods 'under the counter'. By the same token, shopkeepers ran the risk of being unfairly vilified by their customers, some of whom were ready to condemn any price rise, however justified, as 'profiteering': 'One week there was two boats of oranges sunk and that affected the market, of course; the price went up and you can imagine the complaints.'

However, only food supplied in large enough quantities to be available to the masses was rationed. For those with the money to pay for it, there was always a more or less ready supply of luxury foodstuffs. As this breathless correspondent for *Shopping News* reported: 'The mouthwatering displays of foodstuffs at Fortnum and Mason's this week made me wonder whether rationing need worry anybody. If you're short of anything in the food line I'll be surprised if you can't get it here.'

One disincentive to ordinary people might have been the prices luxury foods attracted in wartime. Grapes could be as much as £1 a bunch, a melon 10–15s and a bottle of wine costing 5s before the war was going for £1 5s. Even so, the diaries of 'Chips' Channon recall a dinner party in 1944 at which nineteen car-loads of people dined on oysters, salmon, dressed crab, minced chicken and enough alcohol to get happily drunk. While such events may have been the exception, they tended to multiply in the telling and fuelled the resentment of ordinary rationed members of the public in proportion.

At the other extreme, civil servants worked out an absolute minimum diet, for introduction in the event of dire emergency. It was supposed to be the minimum necessary to sustain life, and consisted of a mixture of bread, potatoes, oatmeal, vegetables – all in very small quantities – and $\frac{3}{5}$ pint of milk. Churchill was shown this 'basal diet', as it was called, and was horrified. He commented: 'Almost all the food faddists I ever knew, nut-

---

FOOD, GLORIOUS FOOD . . .

Pig bins were provided on street corners. An army of inspectors kept an eye on them, to ensure that nothing suitable for human consumption was being placed in them. Should such delicacies as bacon fat or bread crusts find their way there, local residents would be questioned, and it was even not unknown for bins to be staked out, in the hope of catching the guilty party in the act.

eaters and the like, have died young after a long period of senile decay.' The scheme was rapidly abandoned.

One option for avoiding rationing, not affordable for the ordinary member of the public on a frequent basis, was eating out. Coupons were not needed for restaurant meals. During the early years of the war newspaper photographs of ostentatious consumption in restaurants were not banned by the censor, but as food supplies got tighter, the censor yielded to public sensibilities and discouraged them. The Ministry of Food considered the possibility of requiring individuals to surrender their ration tickets in restaurants but dismissed it as an administrative impossibility. However, the problems it was causing greatly exercised the mind of the Minister of Food. Lord Woolton wrote in his diary in March 1942:

> I went to see the Chancellor of the Exchequer about luxury feeding in restaurants. There is a great press outcry against meals in expensive hotels, the conclusion being that people who pay 10s or thereabouts for a meal must be getting a good deal of food for that money, and there's agitation abroad about the inequality of a system that allows wealthy people to feed very adequately off [outside] the ration. We shall have to do something about this, but I don't think the solution is a tax on meals.

Administratively impossible or not, the 1945 Annual Congress of the Women's Co-operative Guild called for rationing to be extended to restaurant meals:

FUNNY FOOD

'We never starved, but we ate some bloody funny things. Best was American dried egg. You poured a thin trickle into the frying pan, then as it cooked it blew up like a balloon, till it was two inches thick, like a big yellow hump-backed whale. And we had whale meat, that tasted strongly of fish, unless you soaked it for twenty-four hours in vinegar, after which it tasted of vinegar. But there was so much of it – great big bloody steaks as big as your plate – that we didn't care what it tasted like.'

Boy, Tyneside, quoted in Westall.

I had never seen or eaten a banana. Where I lived there was a prisoner-of-war camp behind us. One day I was walking to the shops when a prisoner called us to the fence and offered us three bananas (for my sister and my brother). Not knowing how to eat it, we peeled the banana, ate the skin and threw the inner away.

Girl aged six, quoted in Westall.

In view of the cuts in rations which will press with particular hardship upon the working class, the Congress of the Women's Co-operative Guild calls for the adoption of a points scheme for restaurant meals. We have yet to hear of the wholesale dismissal of chefs employed by the upper classes, whose duty it will now be to cook one shilling's-worth of meat, and two pennyworth of corned beef with one ounce of cooking fat per person. We realise that people with money and influence go short of nothing, as there is still unrationed food such as poultry and game, and meals can be obtained in hotels and restaurants. We also protest at the hypocritical propaganda of the BBC and the press in trying to make us believe that everyone is on the same rations.

The memoirs of the wealthy at that time reveal that they were able to live very well indeed. As the invasion threat reached its height in September 1940, Harold Nicolson recorded in his diary: 'Dine with Guy Burgess at the Reform and have the best cooked grouse that I have ever eaten.' 'Chips' Channon recalls the Dorchester Hotel during the blitz:

Half London seemed to be there. . . . I gave Bob Boothby a champagne cocktail in the private bar . . . our bill must have been immense, for we had four magnums of champagne. London lives well; I've never seen more lavishness, more money spent, or more food consumed than tonight, and the dance floor was packed.

One partial solution was a chain of government-run eating establishments, where the general public could get a nourishing meal for a modest price. However, Churchill reacted strongly (and probably rightly) against Lord Woolton's suggestion of calling them 'Communal Feeding Centres', a term which Churchill condemned as 'an odious expression, suggestive of Communism and the Workhouse'. Instead they became 'British Restaurants'.

Even named thus, they did not avoid suspicion on the part of the public, some of whom saw them as an attempt to introduce collective feeding by stealth. At holiday seasons, too, when they were closed, there were questions asked about what was happening to the food normally supplied to them, and why it was not coming through to the public in the form of increased rations?

Another of the mechanisms used by the government was the maximum charge of 5s for a meal consisting of a single main course. 'Superior' restaurants were later exempted from this maximum, leading to a spate of overcharging among 'middling' restaurants. All sorts of devices were used to evade this limit. The Dorchester, for example, charged a 7/6 cover charge and an extra 2/6 for dancing. Wild overcharging for any wine consumed was commonplace, and one establishment was fined for charging a cloakroom fee (the 'cloakroom' being a row of hooks in the restaurant itself). Five shilling maximum charge or not, 'Chips' Channon again notes paying £10 for lunch for three people at Claridges. Again, Home Intelligence reflected public outrage at the apparent inequalities, in March 1942:

> There is growing evidence of a feeling among certain sections of the public that 'everything is not fair and equal and that therefore our sacrifices are not worth while'. In particular, there is some belief that the rich are less hit by rationing than 'ordinary people' for the following reasons:
> (a) they can eat at expensive restaurants.
> (b) they can afford to buy high priced goods in short demand, such as salmon and game.
> (c) they can spend more on clothes and therefore use their coupons more advantageously.
> (d) they receive preferential treatment in shops, as 'people giving large orders are favoured and poorer people wanting "little bits" are refused'.
> (e) they receive preferential treatment as regards petrol rationing. To quote a postal censorship report: 'we can see the Big Bugs riding in their posh cars and poor beggars can't get petrol for business'.
> The feeling of inequality of 'sacrifice' between the Services and civilians, frequently mentioned in these reports, continues. Ill-feeling between the two is said to be growing as tales of slacking in factories, high wages and black markets increase the belief among Service men that civilians are not pulling their weight.

This sense of inequality even translated itself to the police tendency to be much stricter on breaches of drinking and gambling laws in working mens' clubs than they were over similar establishments for the rich. This was even reflected in Defence Regulation 44C, which allowed them to prosecute establishments whose attractions could affect the ability to operate of those

---

LUXURY GOODS

Anything deemed to be a luxury item was subject to substantial reductions in the quantity manufactured. A team of civil servants based in an office in Leicester Square struggled with the philosophical teaser 'what is a luxury?' Thus it was that hair nets, cosmetics and any underwear fancier than the Utility variety came into short supply. At the same time, a host of new products, some of them arguably of little more use to the war effort, found their way on to the market. Wartime shoppers, starved of normal consumer goods, had to console themselves with such things as leather ID card and ration book covers; personalised gas mask holders; Buckley's Balm, for the treatment of the effects of the mustard gas that was never used on us; and anti-vermin jockstraps and gas-proof suits.

engaged in essential war work. Presumably, similar concerns did not apply in relation to the drones gravitating to the kind of gentlemen's clubs portrayed by P.G. Wodehouse. Another Regulation – 55C – gave the police virtual *carte blanche* to close down any establishment to which they took a dislike. The mere name of a club – such as the Boogey Woogey, the Paradise or the Hi-de-Hi – could be enough to get it the kiss of death from the licensing authorities.

Despite the ostensible equality of everyone having the same number of rationing coupons, the system still worked in favour of the better-off. With clothes rationing, for example, they were able to afford better-made and therefore longer-lasting clothes for their coupons, which was important when so few new clothes could be obtained. Thus, the richest people were able to expand their wardrobes during the war years, while those of the poorest were reduced. For the very poorest, who could not even afford the cheapest new clothes, their clothing ration books simply became another desperate source of black market cash, to keep them from immediate destitution. Some rationing was even avoided in the interests of the relatively privileged. Back-bench Conservatives successfully opposed domestic fuel rationing, on the grounds that it was the people with the biggest houses who would suffer most from it.

BUSINESS AS USUAL – THE 1945 ELECTION

In 1945 the public got their first chance in ten years to express their views through the ballot box. It was an election conducted in considerable chaos. Vast numbers of the electorate were scattered around the world in the armed forces, and the electoral registers at home had been thrown into disarray by the wartime mobility of the population.

The conventional wisdom, even among Labour supporters, was that a grateful nation would give the victory to the man who was seen to have won them the war. Opinion polls forecasting a Labour landslide and even by-elections producing huge Labour swings during the latter months of the war were disregarded, especially by the Conservatives themselves.

Churchill mounted one of the most ill-judged campaigns in modern electoral history. His first election broadcast claimed that the introduction of socialism into Britain would require some form of Gestapo. In that same radio broadcast, which one commentator claimed cost the Conservatives a million votes, he predicted that a Labour government would erode people's savings, and also referred patronisingly to 'you, listening to me in your cottages'. . . .

Mass Observation summed up the public's view of this broadcast: 'It would be difficult to exaggerate the disappointment and genuine distress aroused by this speech. . . .' Attlee, commenting on the speech the following day, reflected the widely held view as to who was behind the Conservative election campaign: 'The voice we heard last night was that of Mr Churchill, but the mind was that of Lord Beaverbrook.'

Whichever hands were pulling the strings, the great war leader had completely lost his way once peacetime politics were resumed. As Labour left-winger Ian Mikardo put it during the election campaign: 'I yield to no man in my admiration of Mr Winston Churchill. I think he is the greatest war minister this country has had since William Pitt, but I am not disposed to have another war to give him an opportunity of exercising his talents again.'

These views were reflected in opinion polls. As early as February 1944 Mass Observation had found that 62 per cent of the population was against Churchill as a post-war prime minister. They found that the public saw him as: 'No man of peace, domestic policy or human detail.'

In contrast to Churchill's vituperative campaign, Labour concentrated on the future, did not attack Churchill personally and did not even put up a candidate against him in his own constituency. But if the Labour leadership was not being provoked into conducting a class war through the election campaign, the demand for radical change was strong among the Labour rank and file. Their candidate for Pudsey and Otley was a young Army Major, one Denis Healey. He told the 1945 Labour Party Conference:

> The upper classes in every country are selfish, depraved, dissolute and decadent. These upper classes in every country look to the British army and the British people to protect them against the just wrath of the people who have been fighting underground against them for the past four years. There is very great danger, unless we are very careful, that we shall find ourselves running with the Red Flag in front of the armoured car of Tory imperialism and counter-revolution.

The election results showed the extent to which the population had been polarised during the war years. Labour took 47.8 per cent of the vote and 393 seats, the Conservatives 39.8 per cent and 213 seats. The middle ground, represented by the Liberals, was all but destroyed. Despite going to the polls with great confidence, with the coup of having William Beveridge as one of their candidates (already an MP, having taken Berwick in a by-election in October 1944), they took just 9 per cent of the vote with their 306 candidates and won twelve seats. Both Beveridge and the Liberal leader Sinclair lost their seats.

Colonel Blimp explains: 'Gad sir, I ascribe my defeat to apathy and to the fact that 90 per cent of the electorate voted for my opponent.'

FOUR

POLITICALLY INCORRECT

If the middle ground of politics had all but disappeared by 1945, some extremes of political opinion continued to be expressed throughout the war years. In this chapter, we look at the activities of fascists, communists and others during the war, and start with those who opposed the war entirely – the conscientious objectors.

NEVER IN THE FIELD OF HUMAN CONFLICT . . .

In the First World War conscientious objectors had been the victims of considerable persecution, from both official sources and the general public. Of those who sought to register, some six thousand ended up in prison at least once and over seventy died of their treatment there.

Herbert Morrison, who for much of the Second World War was Home Secretary, had been a conscientious objector in the First World War. During that war, conscription applied only to men of military age. Now it was to be extended to everyone, including women up to the age of 55. At the same time, the criteria for conscientious objection were widened for this war, to cover not just religious beliefs but also philosophical or even political principles.

The conduct of the tribunals also changed. Gone were the questions about what the appellant would do if he saw a Hun raping his sister. Instead, the proceedings were presided over by a judge, accompanied by other worthies. Their questions were supposed to relate to the individual's role in a democracy in time of war. Do they eat foods brought in by convoy? Would they help a child injured in an air raid? Did they obey the blackout (which could be regarded as a form of passive resistance)? Did they grow food (thus freeing up space in convoys for armaments)? Thus, it was possible to demonstrate that virtually everyone was contributing something to the war effort, and the tribunal could go on from there to test the boundaries of the contribution that each individual was willing to make.

About fifteen thousand claimed exemption in the First World War. The wider criteria in the second increased the numbers of applicants to around sixty thousand. Of these, about ten thousand were refused outright, of which half were later prosecuted and, in many cases, were sent to prison for refusing to serve. A small number – about 2,900 – were able to demonstrate such a complete and principled objection that they were given total exemption. The vast majority were given conditional exemption, provided they agreed to take up agriculture, forestry or some similar activity for the duration.

Conscientious objectors were thus able to plead all sorts of cases in aid of their cause. While many did so on the basis of sincerely held religious convictions, the case put by others raised rather more questions. Lesley Stevens of Birmingham sought exemption on the grounds that he was a vegetarian. In case anyone was under the mistaken impression that Mr Stevens thought that, having killed the Germans, he would then have to eat them, his problem was rather that he thought he would find it difficult to maintain his dietary principles in service life.

Others were prompted by a higher source than vegetables. Lesley Blacknell, a clerk from Shrewsbury Park, London, decided not to take part in the war after 'a visitation from the Holy Spirit. Two days after war was declared, my mind was set at rest by a particularly vivid spiritual experience. The visitation directed me to feed my fellow men by agricultural work.' In similar vein, one man based his objection on a series of mystical experiences he had undergone on different occasions, while listening to Beethoven's Ninth Symphony, reading *King Lear* or sitting on top of a mountain. Another confused political and religious convictions:

> I felt sort of queer when I registered at the labour exchange. People seemed to think I was a coward. I am only going on one thing, and that is the Bible, although I have only read one or two pages. This war is the fault of the government and not of the working class. What is a government for, anyway?

One's calling could be a powerful influence upon one's inclination to fight. One case coming before the tribunal, told them loftily: 'I cannot permit any responsibility to my country to take precedence over my loyalty to God. My loyalty will not allow me to be transferred from the career which I have accepted.' This all sounded very grand, until it transpired that his vocation was as a clerk to the London County Council! Artistic sensibilities were also advanced as a case for exemption. Harold Matthews presented himself to the tribunal as an artist. He considered that the prosecution of war did make use of vice and immorality. He thought nudity on the stage had some connection with the war. The tribunal decided to make use of his artistic abilities and offered him the opportunity to work painting vehicles in camouflage. He refused, whereupon they agreed to register him as a conscientious objector, provided he worked in agriculture or forestry. Mr Matthews announced his intention to appeal.

Some offered in their defence membership of the Boy Scout movement, socialist principles or the fact that they were orphans. Others based their religious affiliations upon the most tenuous links; one pig dealer, who claimed to be a Seventh Day Adventist, was asked when he had last attended church. 'When I was fourteen,' he replied. 'Since then I have been too busy.' Another said his religious beliefs were a mixture of Christianity and Buddhism, though he could not say that he was exactly a Christian or a Buddhist. Others were very clear about their religious affiliations. Samuel Turner of Dudley entered his tribunal wearing a cloth inscribed 'Christ died for our sins' across his shoulders.

Few can have tried to argue the case against war in economic terms, in quite the way that unemployed Middlesex insurance salesman Albert F. Johnson did. He told the tribunal that, for the price of the First World War, it would have been possible to buy for the entire populations of Britain, the United States, Canada, New Zealand and the other belligerent countries a luxury house with five acres of land *each*, still leaving enough money over to purchase outright France and Belgium (the entire countries, that is). His application was dismissed, the tribunal adding insult to injury by telling him that his calculations were nonsense.

Not all those who applied for exemption were of the pacifist tendency. Henry Ballantine-Best of Manchester considered that he had been unjustly treated at his tribunal. He felt that the judge presiding over it had been antagonistic towards him from the outset. This may have been something to do with the fact that, at one point, the appellant had to be ordered out of the courtroom for causing a disturbance. Later, as Judge E.C. Burgis was boarding a train to go home, Ballantine-Best drew the judge's attention to his dissatisfaction by stabbing him six times with a sheath knife.

Scarcely more pacifist was the conscientious objector hauled before the court for refusing to work as a fire watcher. He explained his apocalyptic view of things: 'I object to fire watching as it appears to me to be an attempt to prevent the fulfilment of the scripture which says that the world will be destroyed by fire.'

There were even those who objected on the grounds that they supported the other side: 'I believe that the fascist creed is the only thing to bring peace to this country. I believe that all war is wrong because it leads to the destruction of man. I believe we are wrong in taking up arms against Germany because it was Britain's responsibility.' When the tribunal learned that this last case was a known fascist activist, his objection was refused.

There was public concern, not just about whether appellants' objections were genuine, but also about whether they would gain advancement in their civilian jobs while their colleagues were in the armed forces. Reading

Town Council resolved that any conscientious objectors on their books should be given unpaid leave of absence for the duration of the war. Their superannuation was protected, but otherwise they were told to seek alternative employment within the war economy. Others, like Bermondsey Council, simply sacked any conscientious objectors in their employ, in some cases costing them their pensions.

The treatment of those conscientious objectors who went to prison was not always by the rule book. The following remarks were made by a detention centre inmate, and quoted by Grafton:

> What they did was, they used to bring them in, put them in a cell, strip them naked, throw a uniform in, and that's it. You put it on or you don't, and in the middle of winter that's no joke. To reinforce the point, like as not they'd put a hose on him, wet the whole bloody place out, including the uniform. Every pressure was used, but some of these people were incredibly hard.

But there was one fine body of men where there was no hiding place for the conscientious objector. As their national President, Major-General Sir Frederick Maurice, told the press: 'in the British Legion there is no room for pacifists and there is no place for "stop the war" parties and their pernicious groups.'

THE FAR RIGHT

> . . . was it not a supreme tragedy that one of the most brilliant men of our age, who might have talked to Hitler in a language that he would have understood, should have been shuffled off the stage as though he were a criminal?
>
> Beverley Nichols, writing of Sir Oswald Mosley in his autobiography,
> *The Unforgiving Minute.*

Hitler had many sympathisers, not to say admirers, in pre-war Britain, many of whom came to be regarded as security risks when war broke out. At the height of the government's concern about them, in August 1940, some 1,482 British nationals were detained under Regulation 18B. Overall, the importance attached to the far right of politics during the war years was probably out of all proportion to its real significance.

BRITISH UNION OF FASCISTS

> Mosley was in fact a highly gifted playboy. From the moment he modelled himself on Mussolini, he resembled nothing so much as an actor touring in the provinces in a play which someone else had made a success of in London.
>
> A.J.P. Taylor.

Oswald Mosley's British Union of Fascists was the largest and most active of the pre-war fascist parties. Mosley, the product of a privileged upbringing which included education at Winchester and Sandhurst, entered Parliament as its youngest Member, in 1918. He started out as the Conservative Member for Harrow but within six years had left them, spent some time as an Independent Liberal and then joined the Labour Party. He became Chancellor of the Duchy of Lancaster in Ramsay MacDonald's 1929 Labour government, and was given the job of finding solutions to the problem of mass unemployment. When the government rejected his radical and interventionist proposals, involving public works, tariff protection, the nationalisation of the banks, raising the school leaving age and promoting early retirement, he resigned from the government in 1930 and from the Labour Party in 1931. His proposals none the less attracted interest across a political spectrum which stretched from Harold Macmillan to Aneurin Bevan.

Having run out of mainstream parties to join, he founded his own New Party, with the help of £50,000 from the car manufacturer William Morris (later Lord Nuffield). After a dismal performance in the 1931 General Election, this transformed itself into the British Union of Fascists in 1932. In its first two years it attracted forty thousand members, and Lord Rothermere's *Daily Mail* wrote an article entitled 'Hurrah for the Blackshirts', praising Mosley's 'sound, commonsense Conservative doctrine'.

At this stage, Mosley's fascist policies were directed primarily at the running of the economy. It was his subordinates, notably his Director of Propaganda William Joyce, who succeeded in getting anti-Semitism adopted as official party policy in 1934. It was about this time, too, that their public meetings started to get seriously violent and Rothermere's support for them cooled. Relations between Mosley and Joyce also began to cool, among other things because of what Joyce saw as Mosley's reluctance to embrace anti-Semitism with enough enthusiasm. Joyce was eventually sacked from the BUF, ostensibly as a cost-saving measure, in 1937. By the outbreak of war, membership of the BUF had shrunk to about nine thousand. It was the only organisation proscribed under the Defence Regulations, though leading individuals from other groups were also interned.

Once war broke out, Mosley tried initially to maintain a relatively neutral stance, calling on supporters not to be dragged into 'an alien quarrel' caused by 'the dope machine of Jewish finance'. They should instead engage in Civil Defence activities and 'do nothing to injure our country, or to help any other power'. By May 1940 Mosley went further and put his supporters at the disposal of the British defences, in the event of an invasion. He even condemned members of the Nordic League as Nazi traitors. It later transpired that he was not, unlike some of his fellow extremists, on the Nazis' list of potential collaborators.

One of the reasons for the BUF's initial success was that many people simply could not believe that someone like Mosley could have moved so far beyond the political pale. They thought that his brand of fascism was simply some kind of robust conservatism. The Mosleys were well connected in the highest circles and remained so even after he embraced fascism. Mosley was related by marriage to Winston Churchill's wife, and Diana Mosley (second wife of Sir Oswald and the daughter of Lord Redesdale) had previously been married to Bryan Guinness, one of England's richest men.

The BUF was the largest of the pre-war fascist parties, but there were a number of other, much smaller ones. Like many of those on the political fringes, they dissipated much of their energy in squabbling among themselves about the minutiae of dogma. The main link between all these groups and Germany was the Nazis' 'Gauleiter for Britain', Dr R.G. Rosel, until he was expelled from Britain in June 1939.

THE NATIONAL SOCIALIST LEAGUE

The National Socialist League was set up by William Joyce and former Labour MP John Beckett, after they fell out with Mosley in 1937. It enabled Joyce to give vent to his more violent anti-Semitic instincts. He was the American-born son of an Irish-American, who moved the family back to Ireland when Joyce was only three. He grew up among the struggles for Irish independence during the First World War and, as a schoolboy, served briefly as an informer for a government-recruited auxiliary group opposing Republicanism. The family moved to Lancashire, and Joyce initially joined the British Fascisti, a group of right-wing conservatives, whose paranoia about a state takeover by trades unionists and socialists nicely suited Joyce's own feelings of persecution.

Joyce moved to the BUF and then helped to set up the League. He eventually fled to Berlin in August 1939, days before the introduction of the Emergency Defence Regulations that would have led to his detention. There, he began his wartime radio career as Lord Haw-Haw, in the company of other turncoat broadcasters such as Ralph Baden-Powell, nephew of the founder of the Boy Scouts, and John Amery, the son of Leo Amery, Secretary of State for India in the wartime Cabinet. Joyce was, along with Amery, one of the last Britons to be hanged for treason.

THE ANGLO-GERMAN ASSOCIATION

This group originally had quite an honourable pedigree. It was set up just after the First World War under the patronage of Lord D'Abernon, who was British Ambassador to Berlin during the Weimar Republic. One of its aims was to secure better treatment of the Germans following the Versailles peace treaty. Had they been more successful in this aim, they might have helped to prevent the rise of Hitler. As it was, the Association was dissolved when the Nazis took control in Germany.

It reappeared in a more sinister guise in October 1935 at the instigation of an extreme right-wing peer, Lord Mount Temple. Von Ribbentrop, the pre-war German Ambassador to Britain, also formed a sister organisation in 1936, Deutsche-Englische Gesellschaft, which was used to disseminate Nazi propaganda in Britain.

The Anglo-German Association was extremely well connected in high society. Before the war, some of its members moved among a group known as the 'Cliveden set' (named after the monumental stately home of the Astor family, near Maidenhead). Many of this group's members had fawned upon Von Ribbentrop, and regarded Britain and Germany as united bulwarks against Communism. Influential people attended its gala events, including Lord Halifax, the Foreign Secretary.

THE RIGHT CLUB

The Right Club was founded in 1939 by Captain Archibald Maule Ramsay, a far-right Conservative Member of Parliament for Peebles and Midlothian. Ramsay had served with some distinction in the First World War and became a Member of Parliament in 1931. He spent a number of uneventful years on the back benches, espousing strongly Christian and even more strongly anti-Communist views. But in 1938 he came to the view that the world was in danger of being dominated by a conspiracy of Jews, Bolsheviks and Freemasons. He became a firm believer in the *Protocol of the Elders of Zion*.

His tiny organisation of some three hundred members carried out what has been described as 'pro-German activities and secret subversive work, with the object of disorganising the home front and hindering the prosecution of the war'. The *Daily Express* claimed in June 1940 that Ramsay had been selected as the Gauleiter for Scotland, in the event of a German invasion. Ramsay denied it, sued them for libel, and was awarded the derisory sum of one farthing.

Ramsay was implicated in the Tyler Kent/Anna Wolkoff spy scandal, described earlier, and was imprisoned from May 1940 to September 1944. Wolkoff was herself a member of the Right Club and was caught by an MI5 infiltrator of the organisation, Joan Miller. Wolkoff had foolishly entrusted Miller with the delivery of a letter she had written to William Joyce in Berlin, advising him how best to direct his propaganda in Britain.

Despite calls from his constituents to resign, Ramsay did not allow imprisonment to interfere with his parliamentary duties, and submitted questions to ministers from his cell. On his release, he returned to the House. His last act as a Member of Parliament was to table a motion for the reintroduction of the Statute of Jewry of 1290, by which Edward I expelled the Jews from England. This was in June 1945, shortly after the full details of Hitler's concentration camps had been revealed to the world. He was not re-elected.

IMPERIAL FASCISTS AND MISSING LINKS

Despite its grand title, the Imperial Fascist League never had more than two hundred members. It was founded in 1929 by a retired veterinary surgeon, A.S. Leese, previously a member of the British Fascisti. His virulent anti-Semitism is thought to have been brought about by his disapproval of the ritual Jewish methods of slaughtering animals. Leese denounced the BUF as mere 'Kosher Fascists'. Despite the tiny size of his organisation, Leese was one of only two openly fascist candidates ever to gain public office in Britain. He and another Fascisto were elected to Stamford Council in 1924.

The Link was a more extreme pro-fascist organisation, founded in 1937 by Admiral Sir Barrie Domville. Disturbingly, Domville was the head of British Naval Intelligence from 1927 to 1930. The Link was an apologist for every excess of fascism, spreading its views via a propaganda sheet called *News from Germany*, which may have been funded by the German government. Its membership at its highest was just 4,325, spread across thirty-five local branches.

Many other groups emerged and disappeared over the course of the war years. Some were – in their titles, at least – less overtly fascist, wrapping themselves in the cloak of Christianity (the British Council for Christian Settlement in Europe), pacifism or nationalism (like the Nationalist Association, run by a man called Jock Houston, who had been expelled even from the BUF for the extremity of his racist views). Some naive Christians or pacifists found themselves drawn into such groups.

At least four weekly anti-Semitic publications were freely available throughout the war years, and in 1943 an eccentric pretender to the Polish throne, Count Potocki, published what the *Jewish Chronicle* called: 'Probably the vilest anti-Semitic pamphlet yet produced in Britain.'

The Truth about the Jews blamed them, among other things, for 90 per cent of the nation's crime, for pornography and for the Second World War itself. It also claimed that there were no authenticated cases of Jewish deaths under Hitler. Several thousand copies of this tract were circulated.

Even the lunatic fringe had its own lunatic fringe. The Social Credit Secretariat (another front for extreme anti-Semitism) believed that the Nazi movement was itself a Jewish plot! Political and Economic Planning saw Jewish intrigue behind Air Raid Precautions, any form of planning, and evacuation (the latter being a devilish plot to pollute the countryside by

---

THE COMMITTED AND THE CONFUSED

Over and above the organised support for Hitler, there were those individuals who, either for ideological reasons or simply because they were unhinged, would take up the Nazi cause in a public place. Their court cases would appear in the paper after they had been arrested, often for their own protection.

An example of the first category was Elsie Steele, aged 22, of Stamford Hill, who was charged in April 1940 with using insulting words likely to cause a breach of the peace. She addressed a crowd of some three hundred at Bethnal Green, which included many Jews, telling them that 'you won't see many of our rotten government leaders in khaki'. As the crowd grew restive, she warmed to her theme. Hitler, she told them, had done nothing to them; he had simply put an end to unemployment and turned out the rotten yids. Remember, it was Chamberlain, dictated by his Jewish masters, who declared war, not Hitler. So remember that when you kill a German, he is only defending himself, he is not attacking you. I hope I live to see the day when Chamberlain and his rotten warmongers are put on trial for their lives for the murder of thousands of British and German soldiers, too. As for Churchill, we will remember Gallipoli and the Dardanelles.

She was arrested at that point, and later told the court that nothing that she had said had been resented by a large proportion of the crowd. In fact, she said, she was acclaimed at frequent periods. It was in fact the police who had caused a breach of the peace by arresting her and denying her right of free speech. She was fined £15 with the option of 14 days' prison and bound over to keep the peace for six months.

Definitely more towards the bewildered end of the oratorical scale was the self-styled 'Reverend' Nelson Noakes of Didcot, a clerk and supposed faith healer, who was taken into protective custody when he was found staggering through the streets, shouting: 'You have not got much longer! England will soon fall and then you will see!'

The court was told that Noakes was in the habit of drinking cheap wine and becoming abusive. He was fined £1 and the court never learned exactly what it was they would see when England fell.

introducing 'verminous Jews'). The National Health Service and the Beveridge report (and no doubt most of everything else that went on during the war years) were similarly condemned as instruments of Zion.

Later in the war, fascist groups attempted to come back more into the open. From covert activities like painting the slogan *PJ* (Perish Judah) on Karl Marx's tomb, they moved to open public meetings. These were generally poorly attended and often violently disrupted.

THE INTERNMENT OF FASCISTS

The outbreak of war led to calls for the arrest of Mosley and other leading fascists. During the First World War internment had only been applied to aliens, but the close association of Mosley's party with the Nazis prompted pressure for a harder line to be taken against them. Home Secretary Sir John Anderson initially resisted this pressure in Cabinet:

> Although the policy of the BUF is to oppose the war and to condemn the government, there is no evidence that they would be likely to assist the enemy. Their public propaganda strikes a patriotic note. . . . In my view, it would be a mistake to strike at this organisation at this stage by interning the leaders. Apart from the fact that there is no evidence on which such action would be justified, it is to be borne in mind that premature action would leave the organisation itself in being and other leaders could be appointed to take the place of those who had been apprehended. In my view, we should hold our hand. . . .

The law (in particular Regulation 18B, introduced at the start of September 1939) allowed British nationals who were acting in a manner 'prejudicial to the public safety or the defence of the realm' to be interned. By the end of November 1939 only forty-six Britons had been detained under this clause, almost half of whom were subsequently released. However, the Wolkoff spy scandal broke just in time to strengthen the hands of those who wanted more Draconian action to be taken. Revised Regulation 18B (1A) conferred the power of clairvoyance upon the Home Secretary, allowing him to detain any member of an organisation who, he felt, was 'likely to endanger the public safety or the defence of the realm'. A further fifty-nine people, including Mosley, other leading lights of the BUF and Frank Joyce, younger brother of Lord Haw-Haw, were detained within two days of this revised regulation coming into effect. Lady Mosley was arrested subsequently, on 29 June 1940.

It is said that, following her internment, her brother intervened on her behalf with Churchill at a Downing Street dinner party. Churchill's attitude to the Mosleys was certainly in marked contrast to the 'collar the lot!' mentality that he applied to the arrest of thousands of (largely innocent) foreign nationals. Churchill wrote to the Home Secretary, saying: 'Naturally I feel distressed at having to be responsible for an action so utterly at variance with the fundamental principles of British liberty.' He asked the Home Secretary to ensure that they were given hot baths, exercise, books and the wireless, and inquired: 'What arrangements have been made for Mosley's wife to see her baby, from whom she was taken before it was weaned?'

Churchill was also instrumental in securing for her extra privileges, including the right to co-habit with her husband at what had previously been the exclusively female Holloway Prison. The allegedly luxurious conditions under which they were imprisoned were a source of public outrage throughout their internment. Bus conductors stopping outside Holloway Prison would announce the stop as 'Lady Mosley's suite'.

It was rumoured that the imprisoned Mosley led a life of bridge and champagne, with a prisoner valet to fetch him his silk underwear when it had returned from being laundered in Mayfair. While the details of their imprisonment were no doubt embellished by the press in the interests of a good story, and Mosley denied many of them during the course of his unsuccessful appeal against internment, it certainly appears that they enjoyed considerable privilege. They were allowed to cultivate fresh vegetables on a plot of land within the prison walls, were able to have their children come for extended visits and had other inmates to do many of the domestic chores for them.

While initially held in a men's prison, Mosley and his fellow internees used to conduct meetings of what they styled the Fascist Grand Council in their cells and he even set up a registered war charity – the 18B (British) Aid Fund in September 1942. Its ostensible aims were to raise funds for the dependents of internees and to campaign against the legislation that had put them there.

There was further public outrage when the couple were released on medical grounds in November 1943 (she had dysentery and Mosley a circulatory problem). They had to be smuggled out of prison amid cries for their re-arrest and for Mosley's hanging, and spent the remainder of the war under house arrest. However, as *The Times* pointed out:

> Sir Oswald Mosley's detention for three and a half years was preventative, not punitive; no court had convicted him, nor had he been charged with any crime. It was for what the Home Secretary thought he might do, and to prevent him doing it, that he was put in gaol.

THE HUNT FOR A BRITISH FIFTH COLUMN

Overall, very little evidence of active treachery was found among the British population. However, this did not prevent both the authorities and the general public looking for it, often on the thinnest of pretexts. A correspondent to the *Spectator* gave an account of the experience of one of those arrested. He was taken direct from his home to prison, where, for ten days, he was held in almost complete solitary confinement, without even basic amenities such as a shaver or toothpaste and with no indication of the charges against him. Even after a month, no charges had been laid and there was no sign of any trial in prospect. And who was this threat to national security? He was a retired army officer, who had fought in the First World War and had volunteered to do so in the Second. His only crime was that, for just one month in 1934, he had been a member of the British Union of Fascists.

Many who were not even formally accused by the authorities were subject to trial by rumour. Lord Iliffe said there was an 'urgent need for the inauguration of an anti-chatter campaign in Berkshire'. He was one of its victims, with rumours circulating that he was in fact a German and had been imprisoned. The entire substance for these rumours was apparently the fact that he had once entertained the German Ambassador to a day's shooting.

Such rumours were not confined to the aristocracy. Allegations about one tradesman's family became so virulent that they prompted this editorial in the local newspaper:

> I am assured that there is not the slightest justification for the wild and wicked stories that have spread like wildfire and which have been designed to discredit the loyalty of a patriotic British subject, one of whose sons is serving in the forces; his second son is expected to be called up. The same rumour is said to have connected the names of other citizens with alleged 'Fifth Column' activities. Very probably efforts to trace the origins of this poisonous scaremongering will be unsuccessful; having started the snowball on its way they have disappeared into the background, there to watch the results of their villainous work.

The family concerned advertised in the paper, offering a reward for information identifying the source of the rumours. The nature of the gossip was kept tantalisingly hidden from the readers. But their curiosity was satisfied a few weeks later, when a member of the family was remanded in custody for the possession of two unlicensed revolvers. It transpired that Alfred Bird had been the local Secretary of the Imperial Fascist League before the war. The rumours were that he spent his holidays in Germany, attacking Jews, that he had a secret radio transmitter and used to promote the advantages of German citizenship to anyone who would listen to him.

IRISH REPUBLICAN ARMY

The republican movement was entering one of its bloodier phases when war broke out. Five people had been killed and nearly fifty injured by them in the month before the main event against Germany began. From January 1939 they blew up public utilities and underground stations, carried out arson attacks and a bombing outrage in Coventry which left five dead and several injured. They even destroyed the waxwork of Henry VIII at Madame Tussauds.

Because of doubts about the loyalties of some Ulstermen, there was no conscription in Northern Ireland during the war, though some 42,000 of their number volunteered to fight in the British Armed Forces. Nor did they form a Home Guard, since this would have necessitated arming the Catholics. At the same time servicemen returning home proved to be one of the IRA's most valuable sources of new weapons.

Hitler had no doubts as to whose side the northern Irish were on, and some 745 Ulster people were killed in an air raid on Belfast on 15 April 1941. The air raid shelters in Belfast were worse than in any other part of the United Kingdom and, following the bombing, around a hundred thousand people nightly fled the city to find safety elsewhere. Shortly after the Belfast raid, Hitler rather set back his prospects of *détente* with the Irish Free State, when his planes accidentally bombed Dublin on 31 May, killing twenty-nine people.

The British government never forgot the adage 'England's trouble is Ireland's opportunity', and their suspicion was certainly not allayed by Eamon de Valera's scrupulous observance of their neutral status. In 1945 he joined a very short queue outside the residence of the German Minister in Dublin to pay his condolences on the death of Hitler, and Eire was about the only country in the world to maintain diplomatic relations with Germany after VE-Day.

Nationalist extremism was not confined to the Irish, and the Germans tried to cultivate dissidents among all the Celtic fringes of the nation. Even as war broke out, one Barbara Jones was being charged in Cardiff with possessing sixty-nine sticks of gelignite, 'in such circumstances as to give rise to a reasonable suspicion that she did not have them in her possession for a lawful object'. The real challenge for the court might have been to try to think of any circumstances in which a young lady of twenty-three *might* have had sixty-nine sticks of gelignite in her handbag for a lawful object.

COMMUNISM AND THE COMMUNIST PARTY OF GREAT BRITAIN

The CPGB was seen by many as a major potential force in British politics, before, during and after the war. The party had some twenty thousand subscribing members (a membership list that grew with the outbreak of war) and its mouthpiece, the *Daily Worker*, a circulation of up to ninety thousand. Their initial anti-war point-of-view (which lasted as long as Russia remained neutral) was shared by some in the Labour Party, who feared it would descend into a war of rival imperialisms, and by the appeasers on the right of the Conservative Party.

The CPGB led a campaign from as early as 1937, complaining about the inadequacy of Air Raid Precautions for the working people. The blitz proved them to be not far wrong, but this did not stop the police from seizing some of their leaflets during their 1940 campaign. The party was also active in setting up informal committees to represent the interests of their shelterer supporters. They were strongly represented in the Coventry area, and had lobbied strongly for improved shelters there. The major raid on the city therefore proved to be something of a propaganda coup for them. For a time after the raid, the *Daily Worker* was the only newspaper on sale in the shattered city. It lay the blame for what it described as a 'reprisal raid' on 'the big factory owners, the big business and landowning interests' and called for a negotiated peace settlement.

A major 'People's Convention' was held on 12 January 1941 and its proceedings were reported in the national press. Over 2,200 delegates, claiming to represent 1.2 million people, assembled to hear messages of support from people as diverse as Paul Robeson and Mao Tse Tung; among those attending the convention was Indira Gandhi. Within days of the Convention, on 21 January, the *Daily Worker* was suppressed by the government for its opposition to the war. Though most of the national press applauded this action by the government, the *Daily Mirror* attacked it, as did much of the artistic establishment. The ban was introduced despite there being no evidence of the paper having had any effect upon the conduct of the war. Even Herbert Morrison had to concede that: 'Little or no evidence can be found that Communist propaganda is having any appreciable effect upon the morale of the nation as a whole.' The worst they could find to say about it was that it never contained 'a note of real encouragement'.

The Cabinet considered taking further action against the CPGB but ruled against it, despite Ernest Bevin's proposal to imprison party intellectuals as potential trouble-makers. But the government's real problems started when Russia entered the war and a wave of pro-Russian sentiment swept the nation. Stalin, a mass murderer on a scale to rival Hitler, became cosy 'Uncle Joe', and even Lavrenti Beria, the Head of their Secret Police, later executed by the Russians themselves for alleged crimes against humanity, became known as 'Russia's Mr Pickwick'.

The Ministry of Information recognised the problem facing the government after Russia's entry into the war. As they reported to the Home Policy Committee (quoted in Addison):

The Russians are operating against the Germans beyond expectation so that we cannot call Communism itself inefficient. The control by government in this country of industry, the levies made upon earnings and upon capital are all integral parts of the Bolshevik theory, and the combination of all these factors . . . is bound to educate the public into assuming that Communism . . . is either a reasonable alternative to the pre-war system of democratic theory or is a logical sequence to the wartime system of control. . . .

The government could hardly attack the politics of its new ally openly. Instead, led by the Ministry of Information, it set out to hijack initiatives to support them, so that Communist elements in Britain could not claim credit. So, when Communists in Manchester started fund-raising for Russia, the MOI got the Lord Mayor of Manchester to take it over. A body called the Anglo-Soviet Public Relations Committee, populated with 'reliable' people, was set up to oversee a range of liaisons with the forces of the left, and in February 1943, the government was behind demonstrations around the country to salute the 25th anniversary of the founding of the Red Army. At the same time they carefully steered the Boy Scout movement away from what they saw as an unsuitable link with a Communist-backed Anglo-Soviet Youth Friendship Committee.

They were supported for once by right-wing trade unionists, who were equally fearful of Communist influence in their organisations. Walter Citrine, the General Secretary of the TUC, was hard-pressed to say whether he detested the Communists or the Fascists more.

At the same time, critical voices were silenced. Former British spy and anti-Bolshevik Sir Paul Dukes was banned from lecturing to the armed forces, and, at the Ministry of Information's urging, George Orwell's satire of Communism, *Animal Farm*, was rejected by his publisher Faber as being: 'Not the right point of view from which to criticise the political system at the present time.'

> Colonel Blimp explains: 'Gad sir, Lord Punk is right! We can't have the British Empire saved from defeat by Soviet Russia. Dash it, it would lower our prestige with the enemy.'

FIVE

CIVIL DEFENCE: COMMON SENSE?

AIR RAID PRECAUTIONS

Air Raid Precautions began in earnest in 1938. Shelters began to be dug and the process of recruiting a hundred thousand ARP Wardens and sixty thousand Auxiliary fire-fighters started. There were pre-war rehearsals for the blackout, which came into force with the declaration of hostilities.

A whole book could probably be written about the blackout and its consequences. Road accidents doubled as motorists struggled to cope with the unfamiliar darkness. By January 1940 one person in five had had a blackout accident of some description. There were even cases of pedestrians being knocked down and killed by other pedestrians, and moves were made to introduce a 'keep left' policy on the pavements, as well as the roads.

One problem was knowing where 'left' was. It was not unknown for a driver to mistake the kerb for the white line in the middle of the road and mount the pavement. One motorist who did this only discovered the error of his ways after he had demolished a lamp standard and a tree.

In another case, in rather more serious vein, an army lorry filled with soldiers was driving through the blackout along what the driver thought was the main road. In fact it was one of the side roads running parallel to it. They suddenly confronted a brick wall where they expected the main road to be and, in the accident that followed, two soldiers were killed and thirteen injured. But few deaths can have been as bizarre as that of the motorist killed as a result of a collision with a bomber – he drove into the back of a low loader carrying a still-crated bomber to its new home on an RAF airfield.

It was suggested that a 20mph speed limit would help reduce the number of accidents. There were only two problems with this; the first was knowing how the police would enforce it in pitch blackness, and the second was how the motorist himself would know how fast he was going, since lights on his dashboard were themselves illegal in the blackout.

The effectiveness of the blackout as a means of defence may be judged from this account by a German pilot, quoted in Fitzgibbon:

Painstaking observation of the blackout regulations was in Germany, too, based on the belief that the bomber pilots needed only to see the most minute speck of light in order to dump their bombs on to it. This was, of course, nonsense. Neither a

LEAD, KINDLY LIGHT . . .

Over-vigorous enforcement of the blackout produced some of the war years' more ludicrous prosecutions. A man at Bridgend station was arrested, the day after war broke out, for breaking the blackout by striking a match on the platform. The excuse that he was looking for his dropped false teeth did not save him from a fine. A woman was fined for ironing in the dark with her curtains drawn, because the pilot light of her iron kept blinking on and off. Even daylight was no excuse for breaching the blackout – a garage proprietor was fined for switching on a neon sign at midday.

single light, nor a group of lights, was of any help in navigating a plane if there was nothing else to be seen. In any event, London's approximate position was easily detected, even from very far away, owing to the concentration of searchlights. There were a number of recognisable searchlight positions, with groups of massed lights, which our more experienced bomber crews soon learned to use as navigational aids. If they did not expose, and we wished to establish our location more exactly, we would attract their attention and make them illuminate by briefly switching on our navigation lights, or firing tracer, or shooting off our guns at their supposed sites. This usually succeeded in drawing their light.

On the subject of retaliation, the nation's anti-aircraft defences were not in good shape at the outbreak of war. During the inter-war years they had been very much the Cinderella of the armed forces, not least on the grounds that they had very little hope of actually hitting anything. A 1926 exercise by the RAF, firing at a plane flying at a known and fixed course and speed, and at the ideal height for the gunners, scored just two hits out of 2,935 shots fired. By 1938 the entire national stock of anti-aircraft equipment stood at just 100 guns and 800 searchlights, compared with the minimum considered necessary for London alone, of 216 guns and 1,056 lights. A good proportion of this meagre supply was subsequently lost in France. At the start of the blitz Britain had just 50 per cent of the heavy anti-aircraft guns it needed and 30 per cent of the light guns. Only ninety-two of the heaviest guns guarding London could fire high enough to trouble the German planes at their normal bombing altitude.

The AA batteries consequently got the bottom of the recruitment barrel, as Fitzgibbon relates:

Out of twenty-five recruits to one battery, one had a withered arm, one was mentally deficient, one had no thumbs, one had a glass eye which fell out whenever he doubled to the guns and two were in the advanced and more obvious stages of venereal disease. Out of a thousand recruits sent to the 31st Anti-Aircraft Brigade, fifty had to be discharged immediately, twenty more were mentally deficient, and a further eighteen were below medical category B2.

One solution to the recruitment problem was to bring in women, and not surprisingly they proved a very satisfactory substitute for the recruits the batteries had previously received. A new problem was that, because the government was committed to a policy of women working in non-combatant roles only, they could do anything on the ack-ack battery other than actually fire the gun. However, they could shout 'Bang!', if that made them feel any better. In every other respect, they got equal status.

At first, the batteries did not bother firing at their targets, not least for fear of shooting down our own fighters by mistake. This led to bitter complaints from the public about the lack of defence. A decision was then made to fire the guns regardless of their chances of hitting anything, and it proved, if nothing else, a great boost to morale. It also scared the Germans, making them fly higher and causing some to jettison their bombs early and head for home.

Naturally, the defenders could not please everyone. One council called for their local battery to be removed, since the vibrations were cracking the lavatory bowls in neighbouring houses. It was also the case that the guns were almost as great a danger to those they were defending as they were to the enemy, particularly after the introduction of rocket shells, early in 1943. In the first serious raid of 1943 six Londoners were killed by shrapnel from the shells and many more by faulty shells exploding as they landed.

When the first doodlebugs came over, the anti-aircraft gunners saw how these new 'bombers' fell from the sky as they opened fire, and congratulated themselves on their improved aim. On discovering that they were crashing by design, the gunners none the less continued to fire on them, in some cases bringing them down over the crowded centre of London where they could do the maximum of damage. However, the worst of the damage to central London was subsequently avoided by British Intelligence feeding the Germans false information as to where the V1s were actually landing, leading them to make the bombs fall short of central London. While this was good news for the City, it was bad news for Croydon, which – with 142 doodlebugs and a thousand houses destroyed – became the most frequently hit target of the V1s.

> Colonel Blimp explains:
> 'Gad sir, Lord Flop is right! The politicians shouldn't be allowed to discuss the weakness of our defences. It saps the confidence of the War Office.'

In one of the most ill-timed political speeches of the war, Duncan Sandys announced on 7 September that the danger from the V2 rockets was remote and unlikely to amount to much. At precisely 6.40 a.m. the following day, the first of 1,054 V2 rockets to land in Britain hit Chiswick. There was no defence against these appalling weapons, and only the capture of their launching sites eventually removed the threat.

In addition to the anti-aircraft guns, great faith was also attached to the barrage balloons. This was possibly aided by the wartime propaganda film *The Lion has Wings*, which showed German pilots turning for home at the mere sight of the balloon barrage. There were various popular theories about how they worked, including one that they were magnetic and dragged the bombers in to their doom.

The balloons tended to be nicknamed after leading politicians and local dignitaries. At one point 'Archbishop Lang' broke loose from his moorings and ran amok around Lambeth Palace while another (identity unknown) tried to break into Wandsworth Prison. Another balloon fell on the Dover Castle pub in Westminster Bridge Road, where it exploded, killing two people. Ziegler records that, when they were first deployed at the time of Munich, five of the forty balloons broke loose, one of them dragging its cable across an electric railway line, shorting out services for the next half hour.

GIVE ME SHELTER

A survey carried out shortly after the start of the war showed great public dissatisfaction with the shelters being provided. After Stepney was attacked in September 1940, thousands of people went to Liverpool Street station the following evening and demanded to be allowed to shelter beneath it. At first, the authorities called in soldiers to keep them out. But the crowds would not disperse and, when it became clear that they had a near-riot on their hands, the soldiers relented and the gates were opened.

Before the war, the function of the Underground during hostilities was discussed by the Anderson Committee on

> Colonel Blimp explains: 'Gad Sir John, Beaverbrook is right! We must show Hitler we have command of the air, the seas, the land and the Underground!'

civil defence. Some argued for it being closed entirely for the duration, for parts of it were extremely vulnerable to bombing. For example, the Fleet sewer passed over Farringdon Street and, if bombed, could flood the District, Metropolitan and Circle lines at the same time. Other stations, such as Embankment, were also at risk. Other people favoured closing it as a railway and using the tunnels purely as shelters. However, the decision was made to keep rail services running.

None the less, the underground stations – in particular the deeper ones – became the favoured shelters for many Londoners. By the end of September 1940 an estimated 177,000 people were sheltering in eighty stations. The authorities were at first reluctant to let it happen. They feared that the public would develop a bunker mentality and refuse to come out during the day, disrupting essential war work. But it was difficult to stop people buying a 1½d platform ticket and 'waiting for a train' for the duration of the raid. However, as demand grew, people would arrive to reserve their space as early as 11 a.m., and by 5.00 p.m. travellers would have difficulty in climbing over the reclining crowds.

Conditions were at first insanitary in the extreme. Hundreds of shelterers shared a few curtained-off buckets that served as toilets and were frequently knocked over. The less fastidious among them saw nothing wrong in continuing their full range of bedroom activities there, providing some unexpected coaching in the facts of life for younger shelterers.

In order to maintain the train services, the operators painted two lines along the platform, 8 feet and 4 feet from the platform edge. People sitting or lying on the platform could not cross the 8 foot line until 7.30 p.m., when the rush hour was deemed to be over. The 4 foot line could not be crossed until 10.30 p.m., when the services stopped and the current was turned off. Thereafter, some people even slept on the tracks themselves. But not even these proved an entirely safe place to be in an air raid. Bank station suffered a direct hit and a number of the 111 victims died as a result of being blown into the path of an oncoming train. The worst disaster of its kind occurred at Balham in October, when a burst water main led to a tidal wave of sludge that suffocated many of the 680 people sheltering there.

Other subterranean communities formed at the Chislehurst Caves, where some eight thousand Londoners took refuge. Some of these even became semi-permanent homes for bomb victims, and their caves became very well appointed. One even boasted a piano. Some sixteen thousand sought shelter beneath the goods yard at Stepney, and Epping Forest also became a favoured campsite.

After the first month of bombing, there was considerable anger at the failure of the authorities to provide sufficient deep shelters, and at the shortcomings of other ARP preparations. The Communist Party in particular led the calls for deep shelters. Initially, the government resisted these, on the grounds that they would have to be widely dispersed and people would not be able to get to them in the warning time available. They also raised the fears of shelter mentality and of the spread of contagious disease in them. (Not unnaturally, the huge cost was also a consideration.)

The main target of the protesters' anger was the Home Secretary, Sir John Anderson, and he was replaced in a Cabinet reshuffle by Herbert Morrison. Morrison was greeted in his new job by an open letter in the *Daily Herald* from journalist Ritchie Calder:

> I have seen tough London workers, of whom you and I are proud, whose homes are gone but whose courage is unflinching, goaded by neglect and seething with resentment and furious reproach. THEY LOOK TO YOU. Much of the breakdown in the last month could have been foreseen and avoided, or mastered by anyone who understood the human problem of the Londoners. GO TO IT, HERBERT.

Morrison ordered deep shelters for seventy thousand people to be constructed. Not all of these could even be completed. One had to be stopped, as it was threatening the stability of St Paul's Cathedral. Another, near the Oval, filled permanently with water. They were also completed too late to be of use for anything but the V-bomb attacks, late in the war. Even during the mini-blitz of 1944, Morrison refused to allow the public into them, since he had reserved them for vital but unspecified war services (possibly the housing of troops bound for Normandy). He said he was 'sure that these considerations will be understood by the people of London'.

Morrison also put the use of the Underground as air raid shelters on a more organised footing. Two hundred thousand bunk beds were ordered, and proper sanitation and mobile canteens provided. Shelter marshals were appointed and tickets issued to regular users. These could be withdrawn if: 'The holder or any member of his family commits any offence in the shelter or fails to do his share in keeping the shelter tidy and clean.' One unexpected effect of this was to make underground shelter places a black market commodity. Spivs sold tickets for underground sheltering places for 2/6 a time – cheaper and safer than any London hotel.

In some respects the blitz could not really be described as the communal experience of popular myth. Apart from the Underground stations and the other subterranean refuges mentioned earlier, communal sheltering was not at all popular. Only 9 per cent of the population used communal shelters of any kind. About 60 per cent of the population stayed in their beds during raids and took their chances. Around 2.25 million homes were issued with Anderson shelters (named after the Home Secretary). These shelters were semi-subterranean corrugated iron devices set into earth in the garden – and they were thought more likely to kill you by pleurisy than the Germans ever were by bombing. Around a thousand households in Fulham alone applied to have their Anderson shelters removed. Later in the war, there were also about a million Morrison shelters, which took the form of reinforced steel tables kept within the house, beneath which people could shelter during air raids.

ANDERSON SHELTERS

'The Government didn't *build* shelters for you. Council workmen just came with a lorry and dumped the bits on your front lawn and left you to get on with it. We didn't think much of the bits, lying out in the rain, gathering rainwater. Just thin bits of corrugated iron, like some old shed. People felt they'd be safer in their houses, solid bricks and mortar. They weren't going out in the middle of the night to bury themselves in a grave. Then my father saw an Anderson that had received a direct hit; he said that there was quite a lot of it left; the house it had belonged to was just a heap of bricks.'

Boy aged nine, Tyneside, quoted in Westall.

'We had an Anderson shelter at the bottom of the garden. The three of us shared it with Maude and Laura Rowlands (two maiden ladies who lived next door) and their fat old brown-and-white mongrel, Patch. It was very damp. My mother caught lumbago from the damp and eczema from spring-cleaning with washing soda, as there was no soap to be had. Every morning she had to drag herself backwards up the shelter steps, in time to make our breakfasts before we went to school. If you were late, and there hadn't been a raid the night before, you got caned.'

Girl aged six, London, quoted in Westall.

Particularly unpopular were the brick-built communal surface shelters, found in many streets where there were no gardens to accommodate Anderson shelters. They managed to be both cold and airless, tended to double as a urinal for drunks on their way home, lacked even enough light to read by and were considered by many of the public to be death traps, since they looked like a military building and therefore were felt to invite attack. And death traps some of them were, but not for the reason people thought. Due to an incorrect mix of cement specified for the brickwork, some of them were prone to collapse at the slightest provocation. A nearby bomb blast, for example, would cause their walls to bulge out, leaving the 9in-thick reinforced concrete roof to come crashing down on any unfortunate occupants – and earning them the grim nickname 'Morrison sandwiches'. In April 1941 the Ministry of Information was set the daunting task of trying to make these shelters popular with the public. Late in 1943 it was found that 106 of the surface shelters in Hammersmith had been built with just a 3in roof, and that they lacked many of the reinforcing bars required. The builders were charged with a £25,000 fraud.

One other item that the authorities developed for the benefit of shelterers was the siren suit. Anne Valery remembers it, not entirely fondly, as follows:

> A dark, all-in-one garment along the line of rompers, often with elasticated cuffs, and with a zip which ran from the neck to below the waist. The theory behind the design was that it could be leapt into in seconds, and the wearer kept warm while rushing to the shelter and sitting for hours in its damp depths. What the male designers had failed to take into account was that, unlike them, we could not pull out our parts, so that the contrast between its snug interior and pulling the lot down before we could pee probably gave us more colds than if it hadn't been invented.

Not everybody had to rely on siren suits or underground stations. Much of London society moved out of the capital for the duration; Mayfair and Belgravia became strangely deserted. In all, 17 out of 37 houses in Hyde Park Gardens and 13 out of 45 in Belgrave Square came on to the market as the war broke out. For those who chose to stay, the basements of luxury hotels, such as the Savoy and the Dorchester, provided a much more salubrious class of accommodation. The Savoy, sensing a good business opportunity, turned its basements into air raid shelters, a dormitory and a cabaret/restaurant. The American broadcaster Ed Murrow visited this top people's shelter in September 1940:

> We found, like everything else in this world, the kind of protection you get from bombs depends on how much money you have. On the other hand, the most expensive dwelling places here do not necessarily provide the best shelters, but certainly they are the most comfortable. We looked in on a renowned Mayfair hotel and found many old dowagers and retired colonels settling back on the overstuffed settees in the lobby. It wasn't the sort of protection I'd seek from a half-ton bomb, but if you were a retired colonel and his lady you might feel the risk was worthwhile because at least you would be bombed with the right sort of people. . . .

Some took offence at class discrimination extending itself into air raid shelters, and on the night of 14 September 1940, a hundred or so East End residents, including some pregnant women and their local MP, presented themselves at the door of the Savoy just as the air raid alert was sounding. They announced themselves as the Stepney Tenants' Defence League and demanded use of the shelter, as they were entitled to do. This test case was of particular interest, as the hotel was packed with visiting foreign newspaper correspondents. After some confusion, it was agreed that the East Enders could go below but, before they could all take up their positions and protest, the all-clear sounded. The management promptly informed them that they could now only stay if they bought something to eat or drink, whereupon the protesters took one look at the prices and left. The British press played it down, but German papers presented it as the British working classes rising up against their oppressors in revolution. It was a short-lived revolution; no further such protests on any scale were reported.

For those seeking further escape from the blitz, pubs and cinemas provided a retreat. Some cinemas would re-run their programme if a raid were still in progress when it ended, and the Granada chain even offered a package of overnight accommodation and a mixed bag of entertainment.

Incendiary bombing increased as the winter of 1940/1 drew in. There was still no compulsory firewatching of business premises, nor a network of emergency water tanks. Both of these were ordered only after the raid on the night of 29 December, when there was a near-firestorm in the centre of London and water supplies were stretched to their very limits – and beyond.

Some of the failures of civil defence involved cock-ups of inspired proportions, such as when an air raid shelter in Maidenhead was found to have been built right next to a reserve tank containing several thousand gallons of oil. The local paper reported their investigation with heavy irony:

> Naturally, the responsible official has had to give an explanation and to reassure the Council on the point of the safety of the shelter. He has, I believe, told them – and his statement has presently been accepted – that the oil stored in the tank is heavy oil and in the event of a hit by a bomb would not explode, but merely burn. Thus, the occupants of the shelter would not be blown to pieces; they would only be roasted alive. How comforting!

Rivalling them in incompetence, and certainly surpassing them in insensitivity, Fulham Council told some of its ARP staff that it could not afford the steel reinforcement required for their shelter, but that they would pay £7 10s towards the funeral expenses of any of their number killed on duty.

GAS ATTACK

Some of the most thorough preparations were made for a threat that did not materialise. After its use in the trenches of the First World War, there was a widespread terror of gas attack, and tens of thousands of its victims were still around as living warnings of the terror weapon. This fear was undoubtedly not helped by the publication of the novel *The Gas War of 1940* by 'Miles', in 1931, predicting the destruction of London from the skies.

> ### INSIDE THE MASK
>
> 'Although I could breathe in it, I felt as if I couldn't. It didn't seem possible that enough air was coming through the filter. The covering over my face, the cloudy Perspex in front of my eyes, and the overpowering smell of rubber, made me feel slightly panicky, though I still laughed each time I breathed out, and the edges of the mask blew a gentle raspberry against my cheeks.'
>
> 'The moment you put it on, the window misted up, blinding you. Our mums were told to rub soap on the inside of the window, to prevent this. It made it harder to see than ever, and you got soap in your eyes. There was a rubber washer under your chin, that flipped up and hit you, every time you breathed in. . . . The bottom of the mask soon filled up with spit, and your face got so hot and sweaty you could have screamed.'
>
> Children, quoted in Westall.

By the beginning of 1937 civilian gas-masks were being produced at a rate of 150,000 a week, and some 38 million had been issued by the time of the Munich crisis in September 1938. They were neither easy nor comfortable to wear; beards or elaborate hairstyles both reduced the amount of protection they could provide. The Ministry of Home Security also issued the following warning to women during the first months of war: 'The attention of women is drawn to the fact that the temperature conditions inside the face-piece of the mask cause eye-black to run, leading to smarting of the eyes, profuse tears and spasms of the eyelids. This produces an urgent desire to remove the mask, with dangerous results if gas is present.' Waterproof eye make-up soon became available to overcome this problem.

It is not strictly true to say that there were no civilian casualties from gas during the war, but those that did occur were caused by our side. One ARP authority decided to test the public's readiness for gas attacks, and went to a busy street, armed with a supply of tear gas bombs and a loudspeaker van. The fact that the announcer had himself to wear a gas-mask made him totally incomprehensible to the puzzled passers-by, who found themselves rendered inexplicably tearful by the mystery cloud.

There was at first strong social pressure to carry your gas-mask with you at all times; you could be refused admission to places of entertainment or find yourself lectured by complete strangers. Two soldiers, on being sentenced to death for murder at the Old Bailey, were chastised by the police officer accompanying them for leaving their gas-masks behind as they left the dock. But as the months drew on without any sign of gas attack, the practice lapsed. Women began using their gas-mask cases as substitute handbags; small boys found them invaluable as football goal-posts. Among young men, carrying a gas-mask was eventually seen as a virtual denial of one's virility.

THE LOCAL DEFENCE VOLUNTEERS

> The British government is committing the worst crime of all. Evidently it permits open preparations for the formation of murder bands. The preparations which are being made all over England to arm the civilian population for guerrilla warfare are contrary to the rules of international law. German official quarters warn the misled British public and remind them of the fate of Polish *Franc-tireurs* and gangs of murderers. Civilians who take up arms against German soldiers are, under international law, no better than murderers, whether they are priests or bank clerks.
>
> German radio broadcast, commenting on the formation of the Home Guard.

Tuesday, 14 May 1940. Britain had a new prime minister in Winston Churchill, who had appointed Anthony Eden as his Secretary of State for War. That night, Eden made a broadcast on the Home Service that would bring millions of people on the home front into closer contact with the war:

> In order to leave nothing to chance, and to supplement from sources as yet untapped the means of defence already arranged, we are going to ask you to help us in a manner which I know will be welcome to thousands of you. Since the war began, the government have received countless enquiries from all over the kingdom from men of all ages who are for one reason or another not at present engaged in military service, and who wish to do something for the defence of their country. Well, now is your opportunity.
>
> We want large numbers of men in Great Britain, who are British subjects, between the ages of 17 and 65 . . . to come forward now and offer their services . . . the name of the new force which is now to be raised will be the Local Defence Volunteers. . . . This name describes its duties in three words. . . . This is . . . a part-time job, so there will be no need for any volunteer to abandon his present occupation. . . . When on duty, you will form part of the armed forces. . . . You will not be paid, but you will receive a uniform and will be armed . . . in order to volunteer, what you will have to do is to give your name at your local police station; and then, as and when we want you, we will let you know.

Earlier in his speech, Eden had described a new form of warfare – the dropping of troops by parachute behind the main defence lines to cause disorganisation and confusion prior to the landing of larger airborne forces. The Home Guard, as it came to be better known, was founded in large part on the misapprehension that the Germans would try to drop large numbers of parachute troops behind the defensive lines, either to act as Fifth Columnists or in support of an invasion. One of their earliest nicknames was the 'Parashots'. On 22 May, as British troops in France were making their way towards Dunkirk, the Under-Secretary of State for War explained in more detail 'the three main purposes for which the LDV were wanted':

> First, observation and information. We want the earliest possible information, either from Observation Posts or from patrols, as to landings. The second purpose is to help, in the very earliest stages, in preventing movement from these enemy parties landed from the air, by blocking roads . . . so that they are hemmed in . . . from the moment they land. Their third purpose is to assist in patrolling and protecting vulnerable spots, of which there are a great number everywhere.

This mobilisation was part of a wider process to ensure that every civilian played his or her part, in the event of a German invasion. Instructions were printed in local newspapers, though the role models they prescribe for the different sexes may grate on some modern readers:

If the Enemy reaches your Village.
What can you do to help in Defence?

What will you do if the enemy comes to your village? That is a question that everyone who lives in rural England must think about now. Here is some practical advice offered to country folk by an authoritative correspondent.

Supposing the enemy motorised columns sweep across and reach your village, what are you going to do to keep him back? You have your village defenders in the LDVs and the ARP workers, and you have defences, such as barricades, which for a time will keep the enemy back. Everything possible must be done to help these men to delay the enemy, just as in every town every man, woman and child must help.

Naturally, with the enemy attacking the village with motorised forces, ordinary business must come to a standstill and young children must be moved to a safe place. But if everyone were to take cover, the enemy would soon get through, so there must not be any safety first. The enemy must be delayed. How?

The men will, of course, do the heavy work. They can rebuild damaged road blocks, hastily improvising new ones when a fresh attack is threatened. They can dig trenches, they can fill sandbags. They can destroy petrol stocks – invaluable prizes for the enemy. They can rip out vital parts from every car in the village. All this work would be done only on the orders of the officer commanding the LDVs, who takes charge of the defences of the village until the regular military forces arrive – but he will need all the help he can get when every minute is precious.

A message may have to be sent to another village. For this duty, a man with a motor cycle has a dangerous but very important job to do.

There would be important jobs for women, too – not perhaps as dangerous and spectacular jobs as those allocated to the men, but jobs which must be done. They will render first aid to any casualties. They will provide and arrange for food for the defenders. If the food in their homes is exhausted they must fetch it from the shops – take it, if necessary, for the enemy will take it without paying for it if they succeed in breaking through.

If the telephones are still working, women will be needed to send messages – and clear, cool thinking will be required of them.

The boys will have many jobs, just as the boys in the siege of Mafeking played such a big part. There must be messengers on foot or on bicycles. There are endless jobs for boys with useful hands and imagination.

The place for the girl is in the home, helping her mother with food supplies and bandages, taking care of the little ones and seeing they are kept safe and out of the way.

If your village is besieged there will be jobs for everyone but, whatever the job, there is a motto for each man, woman, boy or girl. It is this: 'Don't give in. Don't lose your head. Don't panic.' Remember that every moment gained in delaying the advance of the enemy helps your country.

Within twenty-four hours around 250,000 people had volunteered for the new force, completely overwhelming the organisers. The upper age limit was observed very much in the breach. The oldest known member was ex-Company Sergeant Major Alexander Taylor of Crieff, in Scotland, who had fought in the Sudan Campaign of 1885 and who celebrated his 80th birthday at a parade of his unit. (There was one officer who claimed to have been nursed by Florence Nightingale at Crimea, though this would have made him a minimum of 104.) Similarly, the very undemanding physical standards for entry – you had to be 'capable of free movement', whatever that meant – later had to be tightened up to weed out the obviously infirm.

The press were none the less quick to wax lyrical about the merits of the LDV, seeming quite prepared to believe that they would be able to overwhelm the invading forces with local knowledge alone (which, given the initial state of their equipment, was just as well). This example comes from the *Berkshire Chronicle* in the summer of 1940:

Berkshire's LDV Guard. Ceaseless Watch over Vital Points. But more Volunteers are Needed.

The night watch . . . the dawn patrol . . . silent guards scanning the sunset, keen eyes piercing the morning mists, ears alert for any suspicious sound . . . the Local Defence Volunteers are at their posts.

In three weeks, the men of Berkshire have organised themselves into a miniature army to defend their homes and country from sky invaders – from parachutists and the airborne troops that the enemy might cast upon our land.

The Berkshire LDV force has sprung into being swiftly and silently and the efficiency with which its forces have been mobilised has placed it ahead of many other counties. . . .

Their strength lies not so much in their ability to fight like their brethren in the Regular Army, as in their intimate and expert knowledge of the fields, the footpaths, the lanes and the roads in and around their homes. . . . Any one of these men seeing a hostile parachutist or plane descend needs no map to tell him where the danger has come.

But how real was the threat of the parachutist, for which they had been created?

PARACHUTE MADNESS:
THE MYTH OF THE GERMAN PARATROOP MENACE

On the first day of the invasion parachutists dropped out of the sky like a vast flock of vultures. Most of them were disguised in Allied or Dutch uniforms, others came down in the uniform of Dutch policemen and began to direct the population in the streets.

Thus the *Daily Express* of 13 May 1940 described the German invasion of Holland. Their story was without substance, but it fed the fears of those in Britain who believed the same was about to happen to them.

The fact was that there were no vast hordes of enemy paratroopers or Fifth Columnists waiting to drop on Britain. British Intelligence in Belgrade claimed to have uncovered a German invasion plan involving a massive airborne force of 5,200 planes that would, in between having neutralised the Navy and the RAF and escorted a flotilla of merchant ships across the Channel, drop a force of twelve thousand trained parachute infantry on south-east England. Churchill, a leading supporter of the airborne invasion theory since at least 1934 (when he had called for anti-invasion earthworks on British airfields), was one of the few members of the Cabinet ready to believe it. Most of the others simply thought he had a bee in his bonnet.

The German airborne forces were in fact far less numerous and less well organised than this so-called intelligence would have had us believe. Their attempts to set up such a force, following the example of the Italians and the Russians, had been delayed by inter-service wrangling (with both the Army and the Luftwaffe claiming control of them). It was only in July 1938 that the two existing battalions were united under Luftwaffe control, with the result that only five incomplete battalions existed by the outbreak of war.

These limited forces had been used with mixed success in Norway and Denmark, but enjoyed a major propaganda coup by capturing and destroying Fort Eban Emael, a supposedly impregnable fortification on the Albert Canal in Belgium. This was achieved by landing fewer than a dozen gliders, carrying eighty-five specialist troops, on its massive roof. Many of the other thirty-two gliders sent to attack it, and nearby targets, managed to get lost.

This modest force could easily have been crushed by the thousand or so defenders inside the fort, had they chosen to venture out. However, they did not, and the invaders were left with a free hand to disable the fort, destroying the ventilation shafts and immobilising the gunports. Within an hour, the pivotal point of the entire Albert defensive line had been taken out of action. The raid cost the Germans only six dead and fifteen wounded, and their propaganda made much of this success.

German airborne forces also captured three bridges over the Maas and landed paratroops on the airport at Rotterdam. By contrast, attempts to capture The Hague, the seat of the Dutch royal family, by air were almost completely disastrous. At one airfield, eleven out of thirteen transport aircraft were shot down, while at two others aircraft trying to land were wrecked by runway obstacles and the troops inside them were shot as they attempted to get out of the wreckage.

Only about four thousand paratroops were used in the invasion of Belgium and Holland. Moreover, during these campaigns, the Germans suffered the loss of a total of 184 transport planes and a substantial part of their airborne fighting force. As a further complication, parachute silk was in extremely short supply throughout Europe, and by June 1940 the Germans probably could not have mustered two thousand airborne troops. Even some of these would have had to jump without a parachute (which would no doubt have hastened their arrival in England, but would equally have reduced their usefulness once they had landed).

The Germans were, however, aided by some hysterical and extremely inaccurate reports of events which were brought to England by those fleeing the Low Countries and eagerly seized upon and elaborated by the media. They told of a parachute invasion of some twelve thousand troops, some of them dressed variously as nuns, nurses, monks and tram conductors. The press added tales of hordes of parachuting 'women' and of parachutists near Ostend using semi-transparent parachutes and sky-blue uniforms to make them less visible while descending. Clergy were particularly suspect as disguised paratroops. The Mother Superior of the Breton Convent of St Nicholas was arrested twice on suspicion. However, so far as can be ascertained, not a single nun parachuted into the Low Countries during the invasion.

Quite apart from the usual hyperbole of war, one reason for these stories may have been the keenness of the governments concerned to explain away their unpreparedness for the German invasion. Tales of devilish subterfuge and of an active Fifth Column were equally prominent and, in some cases, equally exaggerated. The traitors who massacred sentries at Gennep turned out to be Dutch-speaking members of the Abwehr. A couple of them, dressed as Dutch policemen, marched a group of German 'prisoners' across a strategically important bridge, fooling the

Dutch guards just long enough for the Germans to produce concealed weapons and start firing.

This all helped to fuel a British hysteria about parachutists that even put our own airmen at risk. The only VC-winner of the Battle of Britain, Flight Lieutenant J.B. Nicholson, managed to bale out successfully from his blazing Hurricane, only to be wounded on landing by an over-zealous Home Guardsman. In order to afford some protection to our aircrew, the Air Ministry gave instructions that only groups of parachutists exceeding six in number could be safely shot (six being the largest number of crew carried by any of our bombers).

The public were also warned that the 'hands above the head' posture of parachutists (as they steered themselves towards the ground) was not in fact a sign of surrender but indicated that they were clutching a primed grenade in each hand to ward off attackers. (The dangers of making a parachute landing clutching two primed grenades did not appear to feature in the Ministry's thinking.)

The press also did its bit towards promoting parachute mania – a correspondent to the *Manchester Guardian* suggested putting anti-parachutist machine-gun nests on electricity pylons, while the *Telegraph*'s letters page yielded the intelligence that German parachutists dressed as Home Guards could be expected imminently and suggested that the might of the British Legion be mobilised to round them up (offering the prospect of inter-service confusion on a grand scale). To add to the chaos, a correspondent to *The Times* suggested that the mobility and local knowledge of the AA and RAC made them ideal for rounding up parachutists, and called for them to be armed. What would have happened if the Germans had parachuted in troops dressed as AA men does not bear thinking about. There were even calls to train gun dogs as parachute spotters.

'In Wapping a parachutist came down and apparently he was partially blinded. He'd obviously baled out of a plane. He jabbered away to the people that gathered around him in some foreign language. They assumed he was German and they smashed him to death. They learned later he was Polish, a Polish officer, which was tragic because he was like a British fighter pilot. This is common knowledge in Wapping. Many, many people will substantiate it, but none of course are prepared to say they took part in it, or saw it happen.'

London boy, quoted in Grafton.

Tests were devised to establish whether descending parachutists were friend or foe. They were to be asked upon landing to say the words soothe, wrong, wretch, rats and those. If they had not already given the game away by shooting you in the meantime, their accents would apparently reveal their nationality (though how this worked for the many Polish and other foreign nationals fighting for the Royal Air Force at this time was not made clear).

Even the Germans exploited the hysteria and, in a broadcast to Britain in May 1940, claimed that they had a force of ten thousand planes ready to drop a hundred thousand airborne troops on Britain. The truth was that after the Belgian and Dutch campaigns, they had just 357 serviceable Ju52 transports, each of which could carry just 12 paratroops or 18 ground troops. Even against the depleted British forces of 1940, this did not constitute a significant part of an invasion force.

THE HOME GUARD AS A FIGHTING FORCE

Having initially established the Home Guard to protect the nation against a non-existent threat, their role changed during the course of the war. The three original functions of the LDV, outlined earlier, became translated in the popular imagination to Look, Duck and Vanish (other derisive variations on the theme included Long Dentured Veterans and Last Desperate Venture). The volunteers produced a wealth of false alarms, with everything from courting couples, swans, barrage balloons and clouds to, in one inexplicable case, a hedgehog, being mistaken for German parachutists, but precious few examples of the real thing. By 1941 the emphasis shifted to static defence, with ever-more-substantial road blocks, which were expected to be held to the last man, pending the arrival of the regular troops. By 1943 they were being trained to carry out ambushes, and 1944 saw the plot revert to chasing after parachutists, who this time were going to be dropped with a view to disrupting D-Day preparations.

> Colonel Blimp explains:
> 'Gad, we should continue in our present policy of victorious evacuation, luring the enemy to England and giving him influenza.'

During their more static 'roadblock' mode, they could sometimes do a good deal more harm than good. The Commander-in-Chief of British Home Forces, General Sir Alan Brooke, put it as follows:

Another form of defence which I found throughout the country and with which I was in total disagreement consisted of massive concrete roadblocks at the entry and exit of most towns and many villages. I had suffered too much from these blocks in France not to realise their crippling effect on mobility. Our security must depend on the mobility of our reserves and we were taking the very best steps to reduce this mobility. . . . I stopped any further construction, and instructed existing ones to be removed wherever possible.

Innumerable manned road blocks, demanding to check papers, proved to be a serious obstruction to progress. Certainly, this was the case for emergency service vehicles, struggling to get to London during the height of the blitz.

The consequences of the Home Guard trying to fight real Germans on the ground, especially in the early days when the threat of invasion was greatest and their preparedness and equipment at its most rudimentary, do not bear thinking about. Many of the weapons they used, especially those they improvised, looked more likely to injure

> Colonel Blimp explains: 'Even if the enemy landed here, victory could never be his. Our people would refuse to issue him ration books.'

them than the Germans. They included unreliable and inaccurate Sten guns; Mills bombs, which had a lethal range rather greater than the distance most Home Guards could throw them; hedgehoppers, which were improvised anti-tank devices intended to be hurled over hedgerows (and which then had a tendency to bounce back at you); and the Northover Projector, whose glass missiles of phosphorous mixture could easily blow up in the firer's face. Catapults were also favoured by many platoons, variously hurling burning petrol cans, Molotov cocktails or anti-tank missiles consisting of a broomstick with a grenade attached. One platoon in the London Docklands improvised a new type of hand grenade, consisting of potatoes with razor blades set into them – difficult to throw, but fatal if eaten by the enemy. The 5th City of London (Press) Battalion even had an armoured car. Their Commanding Officer was press baron Lord Astor, who converted his Rolls-Royce for the purpose.

No idea was too eccentric to merit consideration. One correspondent wrote to *Picture Post*:

> What about using the services of British and Norwegian sailors who have worked on whaling ships? A harpoon can be fired with sufficient accuracy to penetrate the vulnerable chinks in a tank's armour.

And then what? Haul it in? Another *Picture Post* reader even suggested seagoing boats, towing a lightly armoured waterskier equipped with a machine-gun, going in among the invading armada to, as they so rightly put it, 'introduce an unexpected element'. None of this stopped the press from talking up the preparedness of the Home Guard – no doubt for the benefit of civilian morale and any Fifth Columnist who might be reading. This example comes from the *Maidenhead Advertiser* in June 1941:

> . . . several new weapons have recently been perfected for the special purpose of dealing with isolated tanks. These new arms will prove an especial boon to the Home Guard in the event of invasion.
>
> Emphasis on the equipment of this new arm of our defence forces is evidence of how much the Home Guard's function has changed. It began as a unit with the job of warning regular troops of the whereabouts of the enemy in the event of invasion.
>
> Today it undertakes a bigger responsibility. It has the job of harassing and obstructing the enemy throughout its own locality. One of its great strengths is that, being a local force, it knows every nook and cranny of the land. And being an armed local force, it is capable of dealing with small bodies of the enemy on its own ground.

Tank hunting in the ill-equipped days after Dunkirk was likely to be a particularly hazardous enterprise, even for the regular army. The 6th Battalion of the Gordon Highlanders were told to form a 'tank-hunting platoon'. They were equipped for this purpose with bicycles and rifles.

TALLY HO! IT'S THE HUN!

Specialised troops were formed within the Home Guard, sounding today rather like a thin excuse for people to continue their pre-war hobbies. Members of local hunts formed horseback units of the force and galloped around the countryside, on the pretext that the roads might become so damaged by enemy action that their services would be indispensable.

Boating enthusiasts formed an Upper Thames River Patrol, under the command of Rear Admiral Sir Basil B. Brooke KCVO. At a time when other river users were being denied fuel and told to immobilise their craft against the threat of invasion, they attracted large numbers of volunteers for their patrols, using free government petrol. These patrols were, however, entirely successful. Not a single pocket battleship ever penetrated the upper reaches of the Thames.

In Leeds the Cobble Hall Golf Club formed its own platoon, with the object of stopping German paratroopers landing on their sacred fairways. Regular patrols were mounted round the course and, while they were there, what better than to practise repelling invaders with whatever weapons came to hand, such as golf clubs and balls. Now, just imagine that flag in the distance is a German parachutist. . . .

> ### THE HOME GUARD IN ACTION
> 'My father was in the Home Guard. They guarded the main road south, at Kainies Crossing. There was a smithy with a gun-slit in the wall, under the blacksmith's furnace. They had to put the furnace out, before they put the gun in . . . someone had the bright idea of stopping the Germans by pouring petrol on the road and setting it alight. They got hold of a twenty-five gallon drum of petrol, and thought they'd try it. They poured the lot on the road and put a match to it. Unfortunately, the flaming petrol ran down the drains, and out into the Burdiehouse Burn, and down it, floating on the water, still alight. I remember the line of fire spreading, spreading as fast as the burn ran, setting fire to the fields and trees. They had to call the fire brigade out.'
> Quoted in Westall.

Uniforms were in as short supply as weapons. In the early days, they did not even have identifying armbands (or brassards) and had to make their own with stencilling sets. Tin helmets could be substituted by items of cookware, held on by scarves. Early photographs of the LDV were banned by the censor, because they looked so comically unmilitary. Even when they finally arrived, the uniforms did nothing for the organisation's image as a fighting force, as the Commander of the 4th Buckinghamshire Battalion of the Home Guard reported:

> The issue of denim clothing forms a memorable epoch in Home Guard history. If a prize had been offered for the design of garments that would caricature the human form and present it in its sloppiest and most slovenly aspect, the artist who conceived the Home Guard denim was in a class apart. Though marked with different size numbers, it was always a toss-up whether a man resembled an expectant mother or an attenuated scarecrow.

On parade, NCOs avoided making their troops about turn wherever possible, since it caused their ill-fitting hats to fall off. Local tailors would be called upon to cannibalise two sets of undersized battledress into one that would fit a normal human being. Only in Harrogate did the LDV look the part. There, the locally based tailoring millionaire Sir Montague Burton had 1,500 sets of well-cut battledress run up from officer-grade barathea. Naturally, the authorities told him to stop it.

Alongside the equipping of the Home Guard, preparations were made among the civilian population to obstruct and confuse the enemy, should they land upon our shores. Unattended cars were to be immobilised, and anything which could give the enemy a hint as to where they were was to be removed. Milestones and direction signs were removed and station name signs were to be painted over. One inspired wartime photograph shows railway employees dutifully painting over their station nameboard, oblivious to the fact that the name was in relief lettering and thus still clearly visible!

Even private premises whose name gave a clue as to their location had to be painted out, under threat of a fine. This regulation was sometimes applied with excessive zeal. The proprietor of the Shinfield Fisheries on the Shinfield Road was fined 10s for failing to paint out the revealing name above his door. He foolishly thought that, as his premises were some miles away from the settlement of the same name, the law would not apply to him. A correspondent to *Picture Post* had an even more ingenious idea for fooling the enemy:

> With a view to misleading airborne invasion, I suggest a scheme of 'adopting' the name of one town by another town in a different locality. If, for example, all the citizens in, say, Coventry, if met by a parachutist and asked the name of the town, would at once reply 'This is Bristol'. All residents in the same town would give the same reply.

The Ministry of Information had its own line on this matter, which was contained in a rhyme taught to children at the time: 'If anyone stops me to ask the way, All I must answer is "I can't say".'

The Germans ridiculed the early efforts of the Home Guard: 'Churchill has spoken about the Home Guard under arms. We ask – under what arms? Broomsticks? Or the arms of the local pub, with pots of beer and darts in their hand?'

The Home Guard's lack of weapons led *Picture Post* publisher Edward Hulton to organise training courses in guerrilla warfare for them. These were run in Osterley Park, Middlesex, and were hugely over-subscribed. Over five thousand members of the force completed this training, but Lord Haw-Haw was again predictably unimpressed by it:

> Suicide Academies have apparently been set up all over Britain. The headmasters are cunning blackguards who teach their inmates to make bombs at the modest cost of 2s each, how to poison water supplies by throwing dead dogs into streams and how to kill sentries noiselessly from behind. . . . Truly the Lord has afflicted these people with blindness! So bombs at 2s a time are to be used against the German Stukas! The people of England will curse themselves for having preferred ruin from Churchill to peace from Hitler.

Descriptions of the guerrilla warfare training illustrate the improvised nature of the event. The painter Roland Penrose taught camouflage; a

THE BATTLE OF TILEHURST. PUBLIC SHOW LITTLE INTEREST.
DISAPPOINTING LACK OF COOPERATION.

The most outstanding feature of the combined Army and Home Guard exercise was the disappointing lack of cooperation and interest which the civilian population took in the 'invasion of Tilehurst'. . . . During the mimic warfare little information of the enemy positions was received and defenders were hindered by small groups of spectators at vital points. It must be emphasised that these people were a danger to themselves as well as impeding the troops.

The civilian point of view was put to our representative by Mr Arthur Fenton of City Road, Tilehurst, who complained of 'brutal treatment' meted out by some of the soldiers to certain civilians. He stated: 'During the exercise the invading force had broken through and were sweeping up the road. Quite naturally, many of us were in our front gardens watching the exercise. Suddenly and without warning the soldiers turned into the gardens and commenced to round up the civilian lookers-on. The garden gate of at least one of my neighbours was damaged. Many people were forced to leave their homes, the soldiers urging them on at the point of the bayonet.

A forces neighbour of mine, was on leave and was in civilian garb, when two or three soldiers in civilian garb turned on him and hustled him into the road. As they passed me, I heard one of the soldiers tell him to 'Put a ******* jerk into it'. I myself escaped being rounded up, as I had recently suffered a fractured rib and I told them that I would stand no tomfoolery. My wife, however, was standing by the front door and she was pushed into the road and had her frock torn by a bayonet.'

One of my neighbours was so taken aback by the sudden assault that he instinctively grabbed the rifle of one of the attackers. There was a bit of a struggle and an officer, on seeing this, stood in the road, yelling like an idiot and shouting 'Shoot! Shoot! Shoot!' One soldier did actually fire a blank cartridge and injured his thumb in doing so. I got my car out and took him to hospital in it. Another of my neighbours, Mrs Lightfoot, had a disagreeable experience. Troops here dashed into the house and rushed upstairs without so much as a 'by-your-leave'. They forced Mrs Lightfoot downstairs and into the road in her dressing gown.'

Mr Fenton added: 'The whole thing was just like a lot of mass hysteria. At first, some of us thought it was something of a joke, but these soldiers were so much in earnest that they were actually brutal in handling civilians. The whole affair was to my mind ridiculous.'

senior member of the Boy Scout movement taught stalking, and one participant recalls being taught unarmed combat by 'a cripple who stood about 4 feet 9 inches'. Whatever the latter lacked in stature, he made up for in blood-curdling intent. He advised his pupils: 'Forget the playing fields of Eton and the Marquess of Queensberry and remember that no way is too dirty to kill a German . . . they don't scream if you stab them from behind.'

Thus equipped, the Home Guard organised exercises, sometimes with units of the regular army, to test their mettle. The following is a contemporary press account of one such:

Elsewhere, exercises such as these attracted considerable crowds of spectators, to the extent that the combatants would sometimes find themselves tripping over the abandoned bicycles and prams of the onlookers, and the judges had difficulty in seeing enough of the action to decide who had won. These judges were also given godlike powers to restore to life any participant in the exercise deemed to have been 'killed', in order that they could get more practice in before having to apply their skills for real. Some of the exercises descended into farce. Broadcasting House was infiltrated by two of the 'enemy', who gained access by showing passes in the names of Adolf Hitler and Stanley Baldwin and captured the Head of the BBC Home Guard.

How effective might the Home Guard have been, if called upon to resist real invaders? Leaving aside the inequalities of equipment, fitness and training, there was the fact that the Germans took the view, quoted earlier, that 'civilians who take up arms against German soldiers are . . . no better than murderers, whether they are priests or bank clerks'. There was the very real possibility that Home Guard attacks against German invaders would also have provoked disproportionate reprisals against the rest of the civilian population, as did the Resistance in France or the work of the Special Operations Executive elsewhere in occupied Europe.

Perhaps mercifully, their skills were never put to the ultimate test. Even so, 1,206 Home Guards were killed and 557 wounded during the life of the force – a casualty rate of something under one in a thousand. Most were killed as a result of enemy action, but a significant proportion died as a result of their own efforts. The worst single event was a training session demonstrating the workings of a No. 68 grenade in rather more detail than the men required, which cost them six dead and fourteen wounded. Members of the Home Guard also won thirteen George Medals and two posthumous George Crosses.

MORALE UNDER ATTACK

The whole story of the last weekend has been one of unplanned hysteria. . . . Of course the press version of life going on normally in the East End on Monday are grotesque. There was no bread, no electricity, no milk, no gas, no telephones. . . .

The press versions of people's smiling jollity and fun are gross exaggerations. On no previous investigation has so little humour, laughter or whistling been recorded.

Mass Observation, 10 September 1940, following bombing raids on the East End.

Public morale was expected to collapse under the onslaught of bombing. When it did not, it helped to foster the myth that everyone in the areas being bombed acted heroically. Apart from its supposed positive effect upon morale, this myth was useful in helping the government to persuade its supporters in America and elsewhere that Britain was not being defeated. In truth, there was considerable variation in the reaction of communities to bombing, which seemed to depend to a significant degree upon the competence of the local authorities in dealing with the aftermath.

When Goering switched his attention away from London, Coventry was one of the first cities to suffer. On the night of 14 November 1940, a hundred acres of the city centre were destroyed; 2,294 buildings were lost and a further 50,000 damaged. Out of a population of 250,000, 554 were killed and a further 850 seriously hurt. The city was devastated – no shops, water supplies, telephones, pubs or communications were functioning. The rest centres, themselves often bomb damaged, were overwhelmed by the demands upon them. The roads were said to be impassable for a mile from the city centre. Coventry police estimated that in the following weeks nearly a hundred thousand people – almost half the city's population – left the city each night, returning next morning.

> Colonel Blimp explains: 'The Government are going over the edge of an abyss and the nation must march solidly behind them.'

The Home Secretary visited the scene the following day. He had been attending a champagne reception with Lord Dudley, the Regional Commissioner, at nearby Himley Hall, and had watched the glow in the sky over the city. He ordered in a thousand troops and twelve hundred building workers to help with the clearing up. Attempts were made to gauge the morale of the population. Home Intelligence reported within a few days of the raid:

The shock effect was greater in Coventry than in the East End or any other bombed area previously studied. This was partly due to the concentrated nature of the damage and to extreme dislocation of services, partly to the small size of the town which meant that many people were directly or indirectly involved. The considerable proportion of imported labour and the fact that Coventry was economically flourishing contributed to this effect.

During Friday there was a great depression, a widespread feeling of impotence and many signs of hysteria. 'This is the end of Coventry' expressed the general feeling. Many people tried to leave the city before darkness fell. A quiet night followed by a fine morning changed the atmosphere for the better.

There was very little grumbling even about the inadequacies of the shelters and in the town itself observers found no anti-war feeling. There was little recrimination or blame.

Mass Observation picked up similar views, but also made the important link between the state of morale and the priorities of the authorities:

> People feel the town itself is dead, finished, and the only thing to do is to get out altogether . . . the whole tempo [of the operation to restore normality] could have been altered if the authorities had spent 5 per cent of their effort on the survivors, e.g. on mobile canteens, loudspeaker vans to give information, newspapers delivered to the streets, social workers.

The lessons from Coventry were learned too slowly by some of the other towns and cities which were to suffer after them. But after the initial shock, Coventry recovered with remarkable speed. While German propaganda was still warning of other cities about to be 'Coventrated', business resumed, often under the most extreme difficulty. The Morris engine works had lost its roof in the raid, but the workers went back to their machines and, braving the November weather, continued in the open air. Within six weeks, production was back to normal.

The south coast took its share of the attacks. Portsmouth was hit in 1941. Ironically, for a town surrounded by the sea, water shortages were a major problem for the fire-fighters. One raid coincided with an abnormally low spring tide, and the fire-fighters were not helped by the fact that incoming fire brigades' hoses would not fit on to the fire hydrants in Portsmouth (a problem encountered in many areas). Another factor that made the blazes worse than they might otherwise have been was the number of property owners who fled the city at night time, leaving their property unsupervised. Without any fire watchers, small, easily controllable fires soon grew into major blazes. Again, Home Intelligence reported on the state of morale:

> On all sides we heard that looting and wanton destruction had reached alarming proportions. The police seem unable to exercise control and we heard many tales of the wreckage of shelters and of stealing from damaged houses, and were told that some people were afraid to take shelter in an attack for fear of being robbed of their remaining possessions. This seems another illustration of the lack of community spirit. The effect on morale is bad and there is a general feeling of desperation as there seems to be no solution. Some of the trouble is caused by children, many of whom do not go to school, though attendance for half a day is again compulsory, but the worst offenders appear to be youths of 18 or 19, though it is difficult to judge as few are caught.

The morale of the city may be summed up in a sentence often repeated: 'The spirit of the people is unbroken but their nerve is gone.' That is to say, though they have been badly shaken by their experiences and are afraid, they do not want to give in. The ability to return to normal may be seen in the way cinemas begin to fill and shelters empty as soon as there is a lull. . . .

The following are danger points: . . .

(5) Lack of home or school discipline for children.

(6) Widespread looting.

(7) The lack of community spirit, shown in this looting of bombed persons and also in the fact that no attempt is made by the people to organise shelters or appoint marshals, and in the reluctance to take fire-watching duty. The paternalism of the authorities may foster this and it may be, in part, temperamental. The danger should be recognised as, in a crisis, panic may spread amongst a collection of people where there is no group feeling and everyone acts for himself.

Southampton was attacked and, after a second raid, the Bishop of Winchester reported: 'the people broken in spirit after the sleepless and awful nights. Everyone who can do so is leaving the town . . . struggling to get anywhere out of Southampton. For the time, morale has collapsed.'

Part of the problem in Portsmouth was the attitude of some of those in charge of caring for the homeless. A government report into the atrocious facilities concluded: 'The attitude of the official in charge appears to be largely responsible. . . . Apart from a personal horror of communal feeding, he expressed the opinion that it encouraged parasitism and laziness and he did not see why "workers probably earning more than I do should be encouraged by the Government".'

There was also much criticism of the lack of leadership demonstrated by the Southampton authorities, and an ARP inspector, sent there by the Home Office, described their arrangements as 'incompetent'. But, if they could do nothing else, the Southampton authorities at least knew how to prepare for a royal visit. One resident who was bombed out of her home recalls being taken to a rest centre, where she and her children were left to fend for themselves in the clothes they stood up in. Then, one day, they were unexpectedly issued with carpets, bedspreads and toys for the children. That day the rest centre received a visit from the king, who asked the woman if she was comfortable in her new accommodation. On being told that she was, the king duly left. The authorities immediately took back all her newly acquired comforts!

In Swansea the myth of British resilience in the face of bombing rebounded on the authorities, after a local newspaperman went on the radio and led the listeners to believe that the bombed residents were walking around with broad smiles on their faces, having scarcely noticed that anything had happened to disrupt their daily round. This caused great resentment among the local population, as Mass Observation reported: 'They could not possibly have behaved in that way and resented being made to feel they had fallen short of some ideal standard. Such talks do not benefit morale – people lose confidence because they do not reach this impossible ideal.' But it was on Merseyside that the authorities came under the strongest attack for their handling of the aftermath of air raids. Mass Observation talked of almost universal dissatisfaction with their efforts. On this occasion, the Home Intelligence report only hints at some of the problems:

> The people seem fatalistic and there is unusual family solidarity, encouraged by the Catholic element. Though they are dour by temperament and have not the cockney resilience, they stood their eight-day ordeal with fortitude and seemed able to readjust to normal conditions. As in Portsmouth, it was remarked that the morale of the 'near bombed' suffered more than that of the bombed. It was also said that people were ready to help themselves until they realised there was official help available. They then expected everything done for them.
>
> There seems to be some resentment against the authorities who are accused of trying to force people to stay in the city during bombing, by making it difficult for them to get out. Unless they can sleep where they feel safe, there is some fear that they may get out of our control in a new crisis. . . .
>
> A symptom which may indicate fear is the distrust of foreign elements. Anti-Jewish feeling is said to be growing. Jews are said to be cowards who have fled to the best billets in safe areas and who avoid fire-watching duties. One restaurant recently refused to serve Jewish customers. Greeks are also disliked and there are occasional outbursts against the Chinese in shelters, though they give no trouble and are cleaner than the general shelter population. . . . In brief there seems to be a need to have someone to blame, and someone to act as a scapegoat to work off the people's own fears. The prevalence of rumours, such as the story that 30,000 were killed in the blitz, and that incendiary envelopes were to be dropped, is another sign of weakness.

Mass Observation stated the full extent of the problem much more forcefully:

> There has been dissatisfaction in other towns but never with such vehemence from so many sources – from working men and businessmen, Conservatives and Labour, officials, parsons, servicemen, firewatchers, wardens. An atmosphere of ineptitude seems to oppress the town, a general feeling that there was no power and drive left to counter-attack the Luftwaffe. It was being left to the citizens of Liverpool to pick themselves up. . . .
>
> . . . Never before has the absence of information and explanation been so apparent. Not a single poster or meeting, loudspeaker vans only giving information on transport arrangements . . . unprintably violent comments on local leadership.

There were many more rumours circulating in Liverpool than the earlier Home Intelligence report recorded. According to these, martial law had

> 'I met one poor bugger I knew at the time, who'd been blitzed. He'd
> been bombed out and I met him three months later. He'd been living
> amongst the rubble, never going to work. I've never seen a man look
> in such a state. His face looked like a rat. He was really a nervous
> animal and his eyes appeared to be trying to look behind him all the
> time. The bomb had smashed his house and he'd lost his wife and kids
> – he'd just gone beyond, with the shock of such a bashing.'
>
> London electrician, staying in Liverpool, quoted by Grafton.

been declared; trainloads of corpses were having to be shipped out of the
city; there were food riots and peace demonstrations. Despite it all, morale
was said to be high, though the level of anger was higher.

By contrast, some authorities dealt with a similar situation with notable
efficiency. In Hull forty thousand homeless people were billeted within two
days of their last raid, and 110,000 first-aid repairs to houses were rapidly
undertaken. A special information centre was set up and, where rest
centres had been bombed, new ones were set up to take their place. In
Sheffield sixty thousand emergency meals were served in the first twenty-
four hours after their raid; a hundred schools were turned into rest
centres and the school attendance officers were turned into billeting
officers. Their success is shown by the fact that the raid made large
numbers homeless on a Sunday, but they were all rehoused by the
following Thursday.

The xenophobia reported in Liverpool also manifested itself in
Manchester, where the Spanish-born widow of an Englishman found
herself before the court for the rather imprecisely defined offence of 'visiting
air raid shelters where her foreign accent alarmed people'. The court
advised her: 'If you have to go into a shelter, remember not to make people
afraid. You have rather a foreign accent and people are nervous.'

REST CENTRES

It may be argued that the government made too much preparation for
burying the dead victims of bombing and not enough for rehousing the
survivors. They had expected the numbers of homeless survivors to
balance out in some miraculous way with the empty accommodation
remaining. But they had not allowed, among other things, for the relative
failure of evacuation. Rest centres, which had been designed to
accommodate homeless families for just a few hours while they were
rehoused, were often asked to cope with large numbers of people on a

long-term basis. At the height of the crisis, in late September 1940, some 25,000 people were living in London's rest centres, which were run under the Victorian Poor Law system for the destitute and were avoided by all who could possibly do so.

Many centres had virtually no facilities for feeding the people staying there – one was issued with cans of soup, but no can opener – or for caring for them in any other way. They were deliberately not provided with blankets, for fear that those using them would get too comfortable and would not move on as planned (there were only 25,000 blankets to serve an estimated need for 2,500,000 among displaced Londoners). One elementary school at Stepney which was used as a rest centre found itself with three hundred unexpected guests for a ten-day period. They slept on the floor with their remaining possessions and shared just ten buckets for toilets, which were often kicked over and the sewage trodden all over the building. Local government in Stepney was so incompetent that the Home Secretary finally took away their powers and appointed commissioners to run services.

Another rest centre, in West Ham, was itself bombed and 450 homeless people killed. This was another area paralysed by moribund local government. They had made little or no effective shelter arrangements before the war and their response to the suffering of the bombed-out was equally minimal. As one commentator put it: 'It was more than bricks and mortar that collapsed in West Ham . . . it was a local ordering of society which was found hopelessly wanting, as weak and badly constructed as the single brick walls which fell down at the blast.'

Bureaucratic rules also served to minimise the effectiveness of many rest centres, until the volunteer workers decided to ignore them and went out begging, borrowing or stealing whatever they needed to function. One rural rest centre greeted its bombed-out guests with a large sign containing the following uplifting information: 'Behind every social problem is revealed the hidden hand of alcohol.'

Added to these problems was the multiplicity of relief agencies which existed to helped the bombed-out to pick up the pieces of their lives. Tom Harrisson published the hypothetical but factually correct case of a Plymouth service wife with children, who would have to visit sixteen different agencies in different parts of the city after being bombed. In London, it was worse – bomb victims had to cope with six government departments, the London County Council, the Regional Commissioner, twenty-eight London boroughs and seventy other agencies, all jealously guarding their budgets, powers and lines of demarcation. Last but by no means least was the fact that many rest centres kept no records of where the people passing through them were going, thus ensuring administrative chaos in the longer term.

Londoners, at least, faced a further onslaught in 1944, with the arrival of the V1s and V2s. In some ways, these affected Londoners' morale more than the blitz had done. The V1s were random in their effects and gave no respite, coming across in a more or less continuous stream. They also provided a heart-stopping interlude after their engines cut out. The V2s, by contrast, arrived with no warning whatsoever. They led to a further hurried evacuation and other signs of panic, as Home Intelligence reported:

> Evacuation has taken place on a considerable scale among those who could get away, particularly women with children, who are said to be crowding the main line stations all day. Urgent enquiries as to how to get out of London are reported from many WVS and CAB centres.
>
> There is reported to be a growing demand for an official evacuation scheme, particularly for children. People are angry, in the belief that no plan has been put into operation, and attempts to get away are, in a few instances, said to be 'verging on panic'. . . .
>
> Sheltering has become 'the next best thing to evacuation' for a great many Londoners. In some parts there is a general rush to the shelters when a bomb is heard, and men are said to show little signs of the 'women and children first' spirit.
>
> Many more people are sleeping in the shelters, both public and private, than was noticed in the blitz, and some are said to refuse to leave shelters day or night.

For its part, the German propaganda machine vastly overstated the effects of the V1s:

> London is in a panic. All Members of Parliament have left the capital, and a thick smokescreen hangs across south-east England.
>
> The roads from London to the country are choked with refugees. Only a few have cars. Most take their pots and pans with them on hand-drawn carts with other improvised vehicles.
>
> Big Ben's tower has collapsed and the Underground is severely damaged. Oil store houses at the Thames Dock have been destroyed. Never before has the world seen such a sight.

Whatever the strengths or shortcomings of the authorities in the bombed areas, and however strong the immediate trauma of bombing, the resilience of the British public in the longer term took both our government and the Germans by surprise. The numbers of mental illnesses declined, and there was no increase in insanity; suicides were reduced and drunkenness fell by 50 per cent (the limited opportunities to get to the pub and the watered-down beer may have had something to do with the latter); the only area of criminal activity to increase during the blitz was juvenile delinquency.

The German authorities, having spent a long time trying to persuade their people that the British were in a permanent state of panic and near-revolution, accounted for the failure of anarchy to break out in the following terms: 'The British masses, exploited by Jews and other monsters, have nothing to live for and meet their deaths with resignation.' They even paid the British people the 'tribute' of saying that they were a Germanic race and therefore able to withstand adversity. When British raids on Germany started in earnest in 1943, Goebbels called upon the Germans to follow the stoic example of the British civilian population.

SIX

BATTLE OF THE SEXES

Before the war ignorance of matters sexual was widespread throughout British society. Organisations like the Social Purity and Hygiene Movement were influential in restricting sex education in schools and encouraging controls on censorship and what was seen as obscenity in the cinemas and other media. They combined this role as self-appointed censor with some disturbing views about racial purity and the right of science to interfere with people's sexual behaviour. Contraception and other sexual aids had to be sold under pseudonyms; thus Rendel's Vaginal Cap was marketed as 'feminine hygiene' and Damaroids virility pills (the Viagra of their day) were sold as 'The Great British Rejuvenator'.

But the traditional Victorian values on these matters were showing signs of breaking down even before war broke out. Surveys of married women indicated that 39 per cent of those born in the period 1914–24 had had pre-marital sex, compared with just 19 per cent of the group born before 1904.

The relationship between warfare and heightened sexual activity had been understood long before the Second World War. In his 1917 work *Reflections on War and Death*, Sigmund Freud talked of 'war aphrodisia' – the link between violence and eroticism. Originally, it applied only to those in the armed forces, who were directly involved in conflict, but the age of total war brought soldier and civilian alike into the front line. There were periods during the Second World War when the death rate among civilians from bombing exceeded the numbers killed on active service. The sense of living for today, lest there were no tomorrow, found its way equally into the civilian population.

WOMEN IN UNIFORM

> Those ATS girls are a disgrace. They come into this pub at night and line up against that wall. Soldiers give them drinks and when they're blind drunk they carry them out into the street. And we're paying public money for them, too!
>
> Quoted by Mass Observation.

Some 460,000 women served in the armed forces during the war years and a further 80,000 joined the Women's Land Army. At the same time

> Up with the lark and to bed with a Wren.
>
> Saying of the day

the belief that women in uniform were 'an easy thing' gained wide currency. This is reflected in the nicknames given to the women's services: the ATS were known as 'officers' groundsheets', and WAAFs were 'pilots' cockpits'. Even the Women's Land Army had its motto 'Back to the Land' subverted into 'Backs to the land'. Military service was held to encourage a variety of behaviour in women – some of it contradictory – ranging from vampishness, through sluttishness, to lesbianism.

The Wrens tended to receive rather less of such abuse, being drawn from a much more middle-class background and therefore rather more aloof from the male other ranks, but even they were not immune:

> . . . the lower deck consider they are entitled to address any Wren in uniform on the grounds that she belongs to their Service. While it is desirable to cultivate good relations between the WRNS and the Lower Deck, it must be appreciated that in a crowded port with many libertymen ashore who have not seen a white woman for some time, it becomes a matter of embarrassment to be continually addressed by sailors and, not to put it too strongly, to be pestered by requests to accompany them, or to make an appointment for some future date. I am glad to say that on this Station I have personally observed sailors and Wrens 'keeping company' to a considerable extent, but it must be admitted that a considerable percentage of Wren ratings, who are daughters of officers, or of a different social status to men of the Lower Deck, find it most embarrassing to be continually addressed by sailors and even more embarrassing to disengage themselves, without causing offence, from such well-meaning attempts to make acquaintance. On the other hand, respectable women in plain clothes are rarely addressed by sailors thanks to the natural politeness of the lower deck.
>
> Memo, C-in-C Eastern Fleet to Admiralty, 15 August 1944.

Various possible reasons for this view of servicewomen have been advanced. One was that women in uniform were indeed more 'available' than civilians, a proposition that we will return to shortly. Another is that, because they could be drawn into barrack room badinage, it led men to believe that they were so inclined. A third possibility is that the increased emphasis on female sexual activity was used to justify the increasingly predatory behaviour of men. Some mixed army camps had cases of rape, or attempted rape, sufficiently serious to have armed guards mounted outside the female latrines with orders to shoot male intruders. Others have argued that these charges of sexual promiscuity were a respectable outlet for deep-seated male resentment of women entering traditional male preserves. The Markham Committee – discussed below – had its own variation on this last theory. This was that the British were essentially a non-militaristic race and had a deep-rooted suspicion of people – and in particular women – in uniform. Thus they became an easy target for gossip and suspicion.

The reputation for immorality became a particular problem for the ATS, which drew its numbers much more from a working-class population and whose inelegant uniforms (designed by men with few concessions to the female anatomy) did nothing for their image. Middle- and upper-class women wishing to do army-related war work opted for the more genteel and less demanding surroundings of the VAD.

The Government first tried to suppress the rising tide of concern about the matter; then, in November 1941, they set up a parliamentary committee to investigate what they coyly referred to as 'amenities and welfare conditions in the three women's services'. The Committee, under lawyer Miss Violet Markham and with a membership including the redoubtable Dr Edith Summerskill MP, looked in some detail at the conduct of the ATS:

> War gives rise to many rumours. Vague and discreditable allegations about the conduct of women in the Forces have caused considerable distress and anxiety not only to friends and relations at home but to men fighting overseas. Some of these tales have suggested a high rate of illegitimate pregnancy, others that excessive drinking is a common practice. . . .
>
> For the ATS, however, we have been supplied with detailed figures on discharges for pregnancy which prove conclusively how little truth there is in the rumour regarding illegitimate pregnancy in that service. There are in the ATS large numbers of married women and the pregnancies of these women are often, no doubt, carelessly confused with those of single women. . . .
>
> Turning to unmarried women, the illegitimate birth rate among the age groups from which the ATS are recruited is approximately 21.8 per thousand per annum. The pregnancy rate among single ATS personnel is 15.4 per thousand per annum. It must be remembered that pregnancy and birth statistics are not identical, for a woman in the Services – or in any other occupation – discharged for pregnancy may subsequently miscarry. . . .
>
> A number of single women come into the forces already pregnant. According to the monthly returns for the first five months of this year of single women who were discharged for pregnancy, the percentage who were pregnant before entering the ATS varied from 18 per cent to 44 per cent.
>
> We can, therefore, with certainty, say that the illegitimate birth rate in the Services is lower than the illegitimate birth rate among the comparable civilian population. . . .

They concluded that there was: 'No justification for the vague but sweeping charges of immorality which have disturbed public opinion . . . one or two cases which, in the course of gossip, have been multiplied many times over.' In their view, the disciplines of service life were: 'A corrective, rather than an incitement, to bad conduct.'

The Committee showed that the incidence of illegitimate births and venereal disease in the women's services was less than in the comparable civilian population – in some cases half the level. The Committee also said that pregnancy figures were no guide to promiscuity, owing to the fact that condoms were (eventually) issued to servicemen (but, significantly, not to service women). They also argued that the stigma of being PWP (Pregnant Without Permission) was a significant deterrent against promiscuity.

In fact, it sometimes worked the other way. Pregnancy was a guaranteed way of securing one's release from the female armed forces, one where the authorities could not afterwards re-enlist you. The relevant regulation was Paragraph 11 and it was not unknown for a woman seeking release from the armed forces by this means to go and stand outside the men's sleeping quarters at night and call out 'Paragraph 11!'. It rarely took long for an accommodating window – and a route out of the armed forces – to be opened to her.

The same wholesome record for propriety could not be claimed by the Women's Land Army, if this letter from one of its members to the *New Statesman* in November 1943 was to be believed:

. . . they care little about mental activities . . . and, looking for any kind of entertainment, they find their satisfaction in pub-crawling or flirting with soldiers. The girls in my hostel are mostly under twenty and know very well what they are doing, they confess that they had never been drunk before they joined up and that their parents would be very upset could they know of all this 'fun'.

Our work in the Land Army is of great importance to the nation, but sometimes I wonder whether the value of all the tons of corn and potatoes brought in by the girls does balance their really disgusting way of living. . . . The best reconstruction and security plans won't help us if those for whom they are mainly meant are left to develop into amoral and asocial beings.

Others felt that they were tarred by the brush of their less fastidious colleagues. One Land Army girl describes the reception they got in the chapel immediately opposite their camp:

We were in uniform and we sat down at the back. Suddenly the Minister, who was a real old Bible-basher, started thundering about 'heathens living across the road, who hold dances on Friday nights and spend their time fornicating with local boys'. We got up and walked out.

THE GOOD TIME HAD BY ALL

'To girls brought up on the cinema who copied the dress, hairstyles and manners of the Hollywood stars, the sudden influx of Americans speaking like the films who actually lived in the magic country and had plenty of money at once went to the girls' heads'.

Home Office report 1943, quoted in Rowbotham.

Armies have attracted female camp followers from the earliest days of warfare. The vast numbers of women who followed the Army of the Potomac in the American Civil War took their nickname from the General who led the army – Joseph Hooker – giving us the American slang term for a prostitute. During the First World War the French set up their own official military brothels, or *'maisons tolerées'* (blue lights for officers' facilities, red for other ranks), and the Germans and Italians did the same during the Second.

While the official American position on the subject (prompted by church leaders and other pressure groups) was that it would be indefensible to use women as war materiel in this way, individual commanders bowed to the inevitable and made informal arrangements for their troops. General Patton was among the more adventurous commanders in this respect, having taken the many brothels, first in Sicily and then in his part of Normandy, under *de facto* military control and subdividing them for the use of officers, white other ranks and black enlisted men. Any suggestion that the British Expeditionary Force might condone such activity had led to the government being bombarded by requests from organisations such as the Association for Moral Hygiene for: 'action to protect the men of the Home and British Empire forces by insisting that, in France and in any other country where the system of licensed brothels still exists, these houses shall immediately be declared "out of bounds".'

The War Office tried to resist such demands, partly for fear of insulting the French, and partly because the rather more regulated conditions which applied in such establishments helped to stem the spread of venereal diseases. In areas under German occupation, these places also formed an important link in the escape routes for allied airmen, since even the Germans respected the privacy of a lady and her client. Wherever the British army went in the Second World War houses of pleasure (or ill-repute, depending upon one's perspective) grew up to service their needs. When one such in Cairo was bombed by the Germans, the British military personnel inside were officially listed as having been killed 'on active duty'.

On a darker note, many cases of rape by Allied troops against French or German women went unreported or were hushed up. The problem became sufficiently great to lead the Allies to ban all 'social intercourse' (which encompassed the other kind) with Germans, from the spring of 1945 onwards. The ban worked about as well as Prohibition, with many troops considering the $65 fine for fraternisation to be a price well worth paying.

Back at home, the arrival of large numbers of foreign troops was met by a dramatic growth in the number of British prostitutes serving their recreational needs. The most obvious sign of this was the so-called

> ### MOTHER'S LITTLE HELPERS
> 'My father was posted to India with the RAF. In early 1940, the Army took away the family's two cars. While my dad was away my mum had lots of American and Polish boyfriends. In this way we got a little more food. I used to grease my pedal car with butter.'
>
> Boy aged nine, Liverpool, quoted in Westall.

'Piccadilly warriors', the crowds of girls who used to gather near the Rainbow Club on Shaftesbury Avenue (an establishment opened mainly for Americans in 1942). In the blackout they had no need of a room to ply their trade – the nearest shop doorway or alleyway proved perfectly adequate. This also went along with the popular misconception of the time, that a woman could not get pregnant from having intercourse standing up. More difficult was the business of attracting clients in the dark, something which many of them achieved by flashing a small torch at regular intervals. (It has been suggested that this is the origin of the term 'flashing'.) The blackout also made it considerably more difficult for the police to detect prostitution, and ladies of the night were one of the very few groups to complain about the ending of the blackout. The number of arrests for prostitution made by the Metropolitan force in 1938 was over 3,000. By 1940, despite business apparently booming, arrests had halved, to 1,505.

A number of factors helped the trade. In addition to the extra demand occasioned by war, the exodus from central London made it easier for girls to find accommodation in some of the areas of greatest demand. They could now afford the rents, since the arrival of the American forces enabled them to charge hitherto unheard of rates, of £3–4 or, by 1945, £5. It was said that some offered preferential rates to the impoverished British militia, but hard evidence of this is understandably difficult to come by. The volume of demand also meant that they could charge these rates for very brief liaisons, and one noted courtesan – a Miss Marthe Watts – claimed in her memoirs to have obliged no fewer than forty-nine clients on VE night.

Not even a town as genteel as Leamington Spa escaped from the rise in wartime prostitution and licentiousness. Mass Observation reported that its streets were littered with condoms after an evening's partying. Much of this activity came from new entrants to the oldest profession. The town's pre-war prostitutes were forced to move out, claiming that there were 'too many gifted bloody amateurs here for a decent professional to get a living'.

Many of the public ignored government advice to keep away from London and returned in droves. This is Euston Station on 12 September 1944. Railway staff were overwhelmed and Italian prisoners of war had to be brought in to help with the mountains of luggage. (IWM AP 7094)

Many of the children evacuated overseas at the start of the war returned as young men and women at its end. These are about to disembark at Southampton in September 1945, after five years in Australia. (IWM HU36233)

Interned aliens, somewhere in 'the north of England' (but probably Huyton, near Liverpool), fill mattresses with straw for bedding. For some, this was the only furniture they had under the harsh conditions of their internment. (IWM FX 6641)

For some victims of air raids, the emergency services could offer no help, and they were reduced to sleeping in a neighbour's house. (IWM D24235)

For those who could afford it, dining out offered a convenient solution to the problem of rationing. (IWM D13333)

A group of East End Jews pursue their religious studies in their bomb shelter. There was much unfounded criticism that Jews were pushing their way to the front of queues for shelter. (IWM D1509)

British girls dance with American GIs. Their presence in this country when so many British men were fighting overseas was a cause of considerable friction. (IWM D14124).

The *Ladywood* motor patrol boat, guarding the canals of Birmingham against pocket battleships in August 1940. A number of waterborne Home Guard units were founded around this time. Some may see them today as a convenient way of continuing peacetime interests, rather than as a vital arm of our home defences. (IWM)

The Home Guard, formerly the Mid-Devon Hunt, near Chagford on Dartmoor in July 1940. This is another example of peacetime leisure activities spilling over into war, with shotguns replacing hounds and German parachutists instead of foxes or stags. (IWM)

Some early Home Guard photographs were censored on the grounds that they looked too comically unmilitary. This, by contrast, would have had the Germans quaking in their jackboots – London Home Guards in August 1940 being trained as high-speed 'dispatch racers'. (IWM)

A small part of the devastation wrought on the town centre of Reading in the air raid of February 1943. Despite the results being rather difficult for local people to overlook, censorship did not permit the local paper for several weeks afterwards to reveal to its readers that it was their town that had been bombed. (Reading Borough Council)

This spread of the amateur was reported throughout England, a product perhaps jointly of the opportunities presented by an absent partner; the harsh economic necessities of war, especially for the wives of serving men; and the change in the moral climate, brought about by total war. It was also the case that the traditional 'management structure of the industry' tended to collapse, as many pimps were called up for military service, opening up the market to the sole practitioner. Two no-doubt-shocked members of the Public Morality Council reported being accosted by no fewer than thirty-five women in a single 120-yard stretch of Soho street. Another Canadian visitor described the areas around Hyde Park and Green Park at twilight as 'a vast battleground of sex'.

Prostitutes were able to avoid the call-up very simply. They simply wrote 'prostitute' in the box reserved for their profession on their call-up papers. The armed forces did not wish to risk the moral pollution of their girls by such a recruit, and war service (in the conventional sense) passed them by. Likewise, the taxman would not stoop to living off immoral earnings, making the occupation additionally lucrative.

Control of the problem was difficult under the existing law. It was illegal to run 'a disorderly house', as a brothel was still called, but street walkers could only be arrested if they actually accosted passers-by; and even then, all they could be charged with was obstruction. However, the market for prostitution suffered a severe decline after D-Day. The George public house near the BBC, much frequented by US Army personnel and their escorts, became colloquially known as the 'Whore's Lament'.

The abandonment of pre-war standards of morality – or, more precisely, the abandonment of the pre-war dual standards of morality for the sexes – excited a considerable amount of public concern, as Home Intelligence reported:

During the last two weeks, a good deal of comment and concern have been reported at 'the wave of moral delinquency', chiefly among young people.
Sex: particular concern is expressed about:

(a) 'Young girls who fling themselves at soldiers.' Some think that, 'with the growing number of enthusiastic amateur prostitutes', the men are not to blame, 'as the girls lie in wait for them on all sides'; but others blame 'the drunken soldiers who are always molesting women and girls'. The need for more women police is the solution most often suggested; others are – a curfew for all young women, or for U.S. troops, and a ban on the sale of alcohol to young women.

(b) The growing number of illegitimate babies, many of coloured men.

(c) The number of wives of men serving abroad who are thought to be associating with US and Dominion troops.

(d) The lack of welfare and supervision for transferred women workers. The unwelcoming attitude of some landladies, together with the small margin of money left for recreation, is blamed for some young girls' readiness to be picked up by soldiers who can show them a good time.

Home Intelligence, 28 October 1943.

Blame of the girls is more widespread, and sometimes stronger, than of the men. Their predatoriness is particularly censured; some girls are said to be dunning as many as three or four US soldiers to provide for their coming child. Some people are very concerned at what the Americans are going to say when they return home. More women police are advocated; satisfaction is expressed where their number has been increased.

Home Intelligence, 8 June 1944.

The most spectacular case of a woman playing the field in the way described above came to light in a British pub, when two American sailors produced a photograph of their wife to show each other. It turned out to be the same woman and a fight ensued. The two 'husbands' then got together to unravel the mystery and it was found that the wife, Elvira Taylor – or 'Allotment Annie' as she came to be known – was 'married' to six sailors and about to embark with a seventh when she was arrested. Bigamy also enjoyed a considerable increase in the war years, with prosecutions rising from a pre-war average of 320 a year to a peak of 649 in 1944.

But it was not just the good-time girls who were casting aside pre-war convention. Double standards, where a serviceman's extra-curricular sexual activity was condoned while his wife was expected to remain celibate, became controversial after a serviceman killed his wife upon discovering that she had become pregnant by another man. The judge released him without penalty. A letter to *Wife and Citizen* magazine in 1945 set out women's concerns at this, and a shocked nation – or at least much of the male half of it – discovered to their surprise that ordinary wives could be interested in sex!

There can be few of us who have not felt considerably irritated by the one-sided outlook portrayed by the spate of heartbreak articles which have appeared lately on the unhappy plight of Servicemen returning home to discover their wives have been sexually unfaithful. Whether mere physical satisfaction, sought while a loved partner is forced to be absent for years at a time, should be called unfaithfulness is a debatable subject. In the past it was a debatable point whether there should be licence in sexual matters.

THIS IS NO LONGER SO! The War Office, in allowing the free issue of contraceptives to men serving abroad, whether married or single, has adopted the principle that married men must be free in these matters. We civilians have acquiesced in the adoption of this principle in that we have not raised our voices against it. We have not even insisted that the issue of contraceptives should only be made to men whose wives are agreeable. There has been no suggestion of issuing contraceptives to wives, who have had to adjust themselves to living without their service husbands for four or five years or longer.

WHY THIS DIFFERENCE? The sudden cessation of their sex life has been as unendurable a privation to these women as their partners. These women, in facing the hardships of life on the Home Front, have been warriors no less courageous than their men serving abroad. Not only have men and women failed to admit and recognise that a woman's sexual needs are as urgent as a man's, but the pendulum has swung as sharply as ever in the opposite direction, giving the male partner in marriage greater freedom and at the same time attempting to tie the woman more closely. The most biting example of this was shown in the recent acquittal of a young man charged with strangling his wife in Nottingham Hospital on the grounds, claimed by the Justice, that the provocation under which the act was committed (the wife's admission that her pregnancy was due to association with another soldier and her refusal to give the man's name) was such that any man would have committed it in the circumstances.

To man has been assigned the right and protection to satisfy his sexual needs as and how he may please. To woman is denied the right and if she tries to exercise it she may be murdered, together with her unborn child and society is to be asked to wink at the slaughter.

Are we to slip back to the principles of the so-called Dark Ages or shall we go forward?

One problem that was concentrating many minds was the extreme youth of many of the girls who were getting in on the new sexual liberation. The disruption of family life by war had a profound effect upon many young people, and juvenile delinquency was a major problem for all the combatant nations by the end of hostilities. In Britain there was a 100 per cent increase in the number of teenage girls arrested in the three years after 1939 and a corresponding increase in the numbers judged to be 'in need of care and attention'. One London borough reported a six-fold increase in the numbers of teenage girls in need of care and attention in the year before D-Day. As one East End magistrate put it: 'Earlier maturity . . . (and the) jungle rhythms heard by juveniles from morning until bedtime, and slushy movies are all in part responsible for an increase in sexual delinquency among youths.'

Others complained that: 'Girls of thirteen and fourteen have attached themselves to coloured soldiers and others and been able to see films that only have the effect of arousing in them instincts that ought to be unknown to them for many years.'

GIs were held to be a major cause of sexual delinquency among young British girls. A US Army private was paid about £750 per annum, compared with £100 for their British counterpart, and many of them had nothing to spend it on but a local female population suffering from shortages of all sorts of material goods. All too often, pairs of nylons came with metaphorical strings attached – 'one before and one after' was the popular formula. The joke of the day about Utility knickers was 'One Yank and they're off'.

The BBC tried as best it could to cope with the changing moral climate. The 'radio doctor', Charles Hill, conducted a broadcast debate among young people of 16–19 under the title 'Learning about sex'. Dr Hill rapidly

---

GERMAN TROOP-CARRIERS

It was not just American troops that proved popular with British women. In the Channel Islands, the only part of the British Isles to be occupied, Baron von Aufsess, the Head of Civil Affairs in the Feldkommandantur, reported: '. . . the complete amity on the beaches between the German soldiers and the local girls . . . with a few exceptions, the girl will surrender readily enough, provided this can be effected in proper privacy. The Englishwoman is astoundingly simple, effortless and swift in her lovemaking.'

There were soon quite a number of young girls expecting the babies of German soldiers. They were known to the locals as German troop carriers.

---

steered any hint of 'progressive attitudes' back to the straight and narrow of 'thou shalt not', in what was by all accounts a very stilted discussion. Even so, the suggestion by one participant that pre-marital sex with the person you were about to marry was 'not quite right but not exactly wrong' was seized upon by some outraged listeners as the arrival of Sodom and Gomorrah in England.

At least the women's magazines could be relied upon to uphold traditional values. This is the advice on pre-marital sex dispensed respectively by *Woman* and *Woman's Own*:

> This time of all times is not one for irresponsibility. If he loves you as you say, your sweetheart will see the wisdom of patience. Remember, too, the emotions you speak of may well be the result of excitement and unnatural tension.
>
> Anyone indulging in pre-marital sex is an enemy to her country, which does not want to be faced with the further problems of unwanted children born out of wedlock.

THE DISEASE THAT DARE NOT SPEAK ITS NAME

The British government did not have a good record in relation to the sexual behaviour of its troops overseas. In the First World War the Allies' incidence of venereal disease was seven times higher than that of the Germans and their allies, largely owing to their prudery in refusing to recognise that a problem existed. The scale of the problem was such that it could have altered the course of the war. In the first war, the Allies treated a total of 1.5 million cases of venereal disease among their troops.

The Ministry of Health anticipated the problem before the Second World War and, in 1938, put forward a proposal for a fleet of twenty mobile VD clinics to tour military bases. The Treasury refused to fund them. By 1940 they were forced to reverse that decision, partly as a result of the number of British Expeditionary Force members, evacuated via Dunkirk, who brought back their own, very personal, souvenirs of France. The problem continued into the later years of the conflict. During the Sicily campaign British medical officers there were treating forty thousand cases a month. Having no organised plan for dealing with the epidemic, the authorities spread the rumour that it was all part of an evil Axis plan to incapacitate Allied troops through the use of prostitutes.

Similar plots were alleged in relation to merchant seamen visiting neutral ports, such as Lisbon. The increase in the incidence of syphilis was substantially greater in London and the major seaports. In Liverpool it had reached 400 per cent of its pre-war level by the middle of 1941. Merchant seamen bound for such locations were issued with special supplies of condoms, to protect their contribution to the war effort.

The epidemic in venereal diseases among British troops overseas was paralleled at home. In 1942 seventy thousand new cases of venereal disease were reported to civilian clinics alone – over and above these were cases not yet being treated, or those being treated by armed forces doctors. With a growing number of young men in the armed forces, civilian cases were increasingly an under-representation of the true scale of the problem. Even so, civilian casualties from VD in 1942 were more numerous than those from the blitz in the previous year.

A variety of factors stood in the way of the authorities tackling the epidemic. First, the 1916 Venereal Diseases Act imposed total confidentiality on cases, making it slanderous to imply that even a known prostitute was a carrier. Second, the latex for making condoms was in very short supply, following the fall of Burma, and the government gave higher priority to making teats for babies' bottles from such supplies as were available. Third, continuing prudery made the frank advertising of VD treatment centres difficult, and the green light normally used in other countries to denote the presence of such establishments was, of course, taboo in the blackout. Last but by no means least, there was consumer resistance to the use of condoms – the variety distributed to the British armed forces were said to be particularly uncomfortable to use and American GIs liked to boast that they were too small for their own lavish requirements.

It was the arrival of the GIs that produced a real explosion in sexual activity and its inevitable consequence. Cases of venereal disease among American troops rose during the first three months of 1943 from 20 per thousand troops to 60 per 1000 – three times the level among US troops in their home country and six times that of home-based British troops.

Even before the epidemic reached its height, the American and Canadian authorities were growing thoroughly alarmed at the scale of it, and put pressure on the British authorities to take action, as this Ministry of Health memorandum from October 1942 shows:

> Our proposal is that compulsory powers should be conferred by Defence Regulation on Medical Officers of Health to require the examination and, if necessary, the treatment of persons who are named as the source of infection by two separate patients under treatment. . . .
>
> . . . Canadian Military Headquarters have made representations to the War Office –
>
> For many months the Canadian Corps Commander and this Headquarters have watched the increase in Venereal Diseases among Canadian troops with the greatest anxiety. . . . Wherever possible, we have endeavoured to identify and trace the source of the infection, and in many cases it has been determined that one woman has been the cause of a multiplicity of cases. . . .

A new control, Regulation 33B, was enacted under the 1939 Defence of the Realm Act. Its First World War predecessor had aroused much anger for pointing the finger of blame at women for spreading the disease. The Minister of Health was therefore at pains to assure potential objectors that Regulation 33B did not discriminate against women. It allowed suspected carriers of venereal disease to be investigated by the authorities if they were named by two separate people as the source of infection. In theory, it was supposed to apply equally to both sexes. In practice, it was applied almost exclusively to women. Of 417 cases investigated in 1944, 414 were women. The Minister failed to persuade Dr Edith Summerskill, for one:

> What is this miserable little measure that has been introduced? Regulation 33B will provide for the treatment of individuals who have infected two others – nothing more. . . . No two men will inform on a respectable woman who has been infected innocently. This regulation will only get a few people, probably only prostitutes, and a few other unfortunate women. The vast number of victims who are infected are left – ignored. . . .
>
> My final point concerns the women who are informed against. Probably most of them will be prostitutes. I want the House to think of the unfortunate, and probably stupid, girl who has become infected, and who is informed against by a second man, who is anxious to protect the woman who has in fact infected him. It may be that a girl will be wrongly informed against. The result will be that she is labelled as an immoral woman. . . . If this regulation is introduced, it will not only be ineffective, but it may cause hardship and injustice to some unfortunate woman.
>
> Hansard, 15 December 1942.

Summerskill was also concerned about the risk of the disease being passed on from the husband, via the innocent wife, to their children. She wanted to see compulsory notification of the disease, and the transmission of it to be a penal offence, as it had long been in Sweden. Further opposition manifested itself in the form of a resolution at the October 1943 annual conference of the National Council of Women:

> The NCW repudiates as fallacious the prevalent opinion that it is the conduct of girls and women that is mainly responsible for the present increase of Venereal Disease, and desires to emphasise the fact that in the great majority of those fleeting and irresponsible sex relationships by which the disease is spread both partners must be held responsible, and a recall to moral responsibility must necessarily be made to both sexes.
>
> The NCW therefore calls upon the government to consider afresh its whole approach to this problem, and to initiate a bold and positive education campaign which will bring home to every citizen and every household the conviction that all who indulge in sexual promiscuity not only may be responsible for the spread of VD, but are lacking in good citizenship.
>
> Mrs Forster (for the Association for Moral and Social Hygiene) said that the (above) resolution was concerned with the problem of irregular sex relationships. Public opinion and the press laid the blame on the woman. Giving an instance in one district where there were large concentrations of troops, one report said that forty girls under 16 were waiting to go into a Home, and it added 'little blame could be apportioned to the troops'. Girls were the menace and men the victims! . . . Yet how grossly immoral men could be towards girls, many of them young children, was abundantly proved in charges which came before the courts.

By October 1942 rising rates of VD forced the government into launching a publicity campaign describing the symptoms and methods of transmission of VD. This was a bold step, since public references to 'sexual intercourse' were at that time taboo and public reaction was uncertain. Immediately before the war, the national press had refused point-blank to carry such information on its pages. At the same time ignorance about the disease was rife: among the myths current then were that you could only catch VD off a professional prostitute and that sex with a virgin would cure you; that you could also rid yourself of it by 'passing it on' to another; it could be caught off toilet seats or from second-hand clothes; and one clergyman who contracted the disease swore that it was as a result of being splashed by the wheel of a passing cart!

Again, parts of the campaign gave the distinct impression that the transmission of the disease was all women's fault. One particularly striking advertisement showed a skull wearing a woman's hat, asking 'Hello boy friend, coming MY way?' and warning that 'the "easy" girlfriend spreads syphilis and gonorrhoea'. Another showed a woman leaning on a street corner with obvious intent, and the warning that 'syphilis and gonorrhoea are easy to get'.

SEX AND THE STAGE

The wartime descent into permissiveness had its parallel in the theatre, but fortunately the Lord Chamberlain was on hand to save us from ourselves. For centuries, this member of the royal household had arbitrarily exercised his absolute power to prevent the staging of anything that was not to his taste. In April 1940 his attention turned to strip tease and the *Birmingham Mail*, for one, thoroughly approved:

'The wonder is that the Lord Chamberlain did not long ago find a means of banning from theatres and music halls that decadent and vulgar importation from the United States known as 'strip tease'. It is, as its name quite frankly implies, a direct appeal to prurience; and what has made it worse has been the profit motive. But nobody has yet confessed to an understanding of our stage censorship – least of all the dignitaries who have held the exalted post of Lord Chancellor!'

A conference was held in St James's Palace on 'Suggestive nudity and impropriety of gesture and speech' (a sure-fire crowd-puller of a title for an event). In the course of it:

'The point was made that indecent shows have tended to increase since the outbreak of war. This is something which must not be allowed to develop by a nation which is fighting above all things for the moral standards implicit in the Christian code; and which cannot afford to flirt with the forces of decadence. . . .

'It may also be said that the ban on suggested nudity, which is to apply to all licensed theatres and cinemas throughout England and Wales, will be welcomed as wholeheartedly by the bulk of stage artists as by the mass of people of wholesome instincts. Here and there, there are to be found "strip tease artistes", so called – mostly alien pioneers – who may be said genuinely to "glory in their shame"; just as willing patrons are not lacking, for the prurient of mind we have always with us. But many a decent chorus girl or soubrette has had to choose between losing her livelihood and accepting the indignity of following this nasty craze at the bidding of her employers. It is a choice which no girl should have to make; and though there may be occasions, even in the theatrical stage, when nudity or near-nudity is not indecent, no amount of inspired prating of "art" and "form" can excuse this species of managerial coercion.'

None the less, the vast majority (92 per cent) of the public – of both sexes – agreed it was right to inform people about VD. One consequence of the campaign was that the incidence of infection fell by about two-thirds in the last years of the war (with something of a blip of gay abandon marking the introduction of the 'one-shot' cure offered by penicillin in 1944). It is estimated that the publicity campaign saved about fifteen thousand men falling prey to the disease before D-Day – the equivalent of an infantry division. It could well have had a marked impact on the outcome of the landings.

MARRIAGE, INFIDELITY, ILLEGITIMACY, DIVORCE

British husbands serving overseas were worried about the influx of affluent and attractive foreign servicemen while they were away, a concern which both sides in the war tried to play on with the black propaganda described elsewhere in the book. These concerns were focused by the case of Annette Pepper, a Brighton housewife whose husband was a prisoner-of-war. In his absence she had formed a relationship with a Canadian military policeman, Charles Gaultier. When she broke off the relationship to go with someone else, he machine-gunned her, a crime for which he was hanged at Wandsworth in September 1943.

Other such crimes, when committed by an American serviceman, did not find their way into the British criminal statistics. US troops were subject to American military discipline, not British law – even in the case where a GI shot an English soldier in a British pub. American public opinion apparently could not cope with the idea that the ungrateful English would thus persecute one of their boys, sent over to help them. Canadian troops were not subject to a similar dispensation, and this sometimes gives rise to the mistaken impression that they were responsible for more wartime crime than their American counterparts.

Illegitimacy saw a substantial increase during the war years, but the figures do not always tell the full story. In the First World War, for example, there was a 30 per cent increase in the proportion of births that were illegitimate, but the rapid decline in the overall birth-rate meant that the actual number of births out of wedlock did not increase. In the Second World War both the percentages and the actual numbers of illegitimate births rose, from a 1939 figure of 4.4 per 1000 to a wartime peak in 1945 of 9.1 per 1000. Based on pre-war trends, about 100,000 of these births might have been regularised by shotgun weddings had not the disruption of the war got in the way.

A wartime study in Birmingham showed that around a third of all illegitimate births recorded were to married women. Even this may have understated the case, since a child born to a married woman was deemed to be legitimate unless the mother chose to register it otherwise. A further sign of the times was a threefold rise in the numbers prosecuted for trying to procure an abortion. However, the numbers involved were relatively small, and police knowledge of these cases probably represents the very small tip of a very large iceberg.

In one unexpected way, wartime conditions militated against divorce. *Reynolds News* reported in December 1939 that: 'West End solicitors, who before the war netted five figure incomes from divorce cases, have been heavily hit by the blackout. In the winter months at any rate private enquiry agents are helpless. Adultery cannot be proved because identification is impossible in pitch darkness.'

In other respects, war conditions bought about a dramatic increase in the incidence of marital breakdown. The annual average rate of divorces over the period 1941–5 was almost twice that for 1936–40, and the high rates continued into the post-war years. However, this change had begun before the war, with new legislation in 1937 making it easier to obtain a divorce. In the final two years before the outbreak of war, the rate was 60 per cent up on the preceding two years. But not everybody found it equally easy to resolve their marital problems, as Home Intelligence reported in May 1941:

> There is a considerable increase in the number of people seeking a divorce. This is stated to be due to hasty and ill-considered marriages, thanks to the imminence of calling up, or to one of a couple, who have lived apart for many years, now wishing to marry a member of the Forces. The number of Poor Persons' Lawyers is greatly reduced, and as a result, many people are having to wait over a year before their cases can be begun. Richer people who can afford the minimal cost of £50 can have their cases heard at once, and this naturally leads to much class ill-feeling.

One change during the war years was in terms of who initiated the divorce. Before the war, it was the wife in a slight majority of cases. This shifted to a slight majority of husbands during the war as a whole, though the final year of the war saw a dramatic eightfold rise in the number of men petitioning for divorce on the grounds of their wives' adultery. Adultery petitions increased by 100 per cent each year from 1942 onwards, and in 1945 two out of three divorce petitions were filed by men. One of the reasons for this may have been the existence of an army welfare scheme, which made it easier and cheaper for the husband to initiate proceedings.

THE LOVE THAT DARE NOT SPEAK ITS NAME

> 'Homosexuality had been on the increase among the upper classes for a couple of generations, though almost unknown among working people. The upper class

boarding school system of keeping boy and girl away from each other was responsible. In most cases the adolescent homosexual became sexually normal on leaving school; but a large minority of the more emotional young people could not shake off the fascination of perversity. In university circles, homosexuality no longer seemed a sign of continued adolescence.'

Graves and Hodge, *A Social History of Great Britain* (1941) quoted in Taylor.

Homosexuality presented a real dilemma for the British Army in the Second World War, just as it had in other conflicts. The official line in King's Regulations was that: 'Confirmed homosexuals, whose rehabilitation is unlikely, should be removed from the Army by the most expeditious and appropriate means.'

An Army study accused homosexuals of dominating the male groups they were in, of finding it impossible to adopt a passive position of obeying orders and of being 'a foreign body in the social microcosm'. The US Army went further, labelling them 'sexual psychopaths'. Yet, prior to the Second World War, the Americans had no procedure for vetting new recruits for their sexual inclinations and the process thereafter tended to be perfunctory in the extreme. Based upon crude stereotypes of camp effeminate behaviour, their vetting excluded only four or five thousand Americans from serving in the armed forces throughout the entire war. However, one of the few studies of gay soldiers in the US Army in the war showed their average performance to be well above the average for the service as a whole, and history is replete with cases of the valour shown by avowedly homosexual troops.

Had the armed forces made serious attempts to weed out all its homosexual members, they would have been seriously – in some cases perhaps fatally – weakened. In practice, the approach was variously to ignore or cover up cases, to offer only mild punishment, or to invalid others out, along with the offer of medical treatment or advice (which often went along the lines of 'try to find yourself a good woman and forget about it'). Only in cases of flagrant breaches of discipline (by which was meant things like relationships between officers and other ranks, thereby corrupting the line of command, or homosexual encounters with the local population) was court-martial countenanced. The Americans introduced the new category of 'undesirable discharge' – which was neither honourable nor dishonourable – for dealing with those found guilty of such offences against military discipline.

None the less the stigma of being found out was great enough to push some members of the forces over the brink. By no means unique was the British sergeant who took to leaving letters from a fake 'son' around the barracks, in an attempt to disguise his true inclinations. He ended up attempting suicide and asking, while being treated in hospital, to be castrated or imprisoned. One British Army psychiatrist estimated that 4 per cent of all military psychological cases were related to homosexuality in one form or another – some think this to be a very modest estimate.

The Germans introduced far more Draconian measures – up to and including the death sentence – for members of their armed forces found guilty of homosexuality. But even this did not prevent the number of cases prosecuted increasing by 50 per cent between 1943 and 1944. Even so, the eight thousand or so Germans court-martialled probably represented only a fraction of the true extent of the practice. It is likely that the incidence at the front line would have been higher than among the population as a whole. The enforced company of a large number of young men, without women, may result in what has been described as 'emergency' or 'deprivation' homosexuality, and the psychological pressures of war – such as prolonged bombardment – were known to lead to temporary homosexual liaisons, even if one of the parties was not normally so inclined.

Whatever their official distaste for homosexuality, most of the combatant nations were perfectly content to harness its potential for espionage. Both the Americans and the Germans maintained 'bugged' homosexual brothels in New York, at least prior to America entering the war, where visitors would be relieved of their money and any intelligence they were careless enough to pass on. Britain, meanwhile, was employing the likes of Anthony Blunt at the very centre of their Military Intelligence operations. Blunt made widespread use of homosexual blackmail to secure the participation of others in espionage. Unfortunately for Britain, the organisation he was really working for was Russian Intelligence.

By contrast, lesbianism, a disciplinary rather than a criminal offence as far as the military were concerned, was treated relatively leniently. Guidance entitled 'A special problem' was prepared but never widely distributed, apparently for fear of drawing attention to the problem. Most cases were dealt with by discreet postings, to separate the couple concerned. Only a small number of what were described as 'very promiscuous lesbians' were discharged from the service.

SEVEN

CARELESS TALK

It has come to my knowledge that information which might be of great value to the enemy is being discussed in hotels, bars and general meeting places. It is the duty of every citizen to refrain from discussing with their friends and acquaintances any information such as movement of troops, numbers of troops, units, stations and similar military information.

The enemy spy system is extensive and a chance remark made in complete innocence may have disastrous effects. All ranks of the forces of the Crown are forbidden to discuss in public or in private any matters concerning military or defence affairs. Failure to comply with this warning will result in severe penalties for all concerned.

Notice widely displayed in the Aldershot area.

PRESS FREEDOM

One of the freedoms the British were no doubt fighting to defend was an independent press. Britons looked with a mixture of pity and contempt at Dr Goebbels' efforts to tell the German people what to think. Had they but known it, the government of Neville Chamberlain that led Britain through appeasement into the war exercised a degree of control over the press that modern spin doctors could only dream about. After hostilities were over, a Royal Commission into the Press investigated how Chamberlain's government had gained such overwhelming support from the press for the policy of appeasement. The story was one of a complex web of informal links between government and press that reduced the media barons to the status of politicians' mouthpieces.

Even as Chancellor of the Exchequer, Neville Chamberlain proved to be an adept user of the lobby system. Yet his treatment of the press was arrogant, bordering on the contemptuous. He would refuse to accept questions with less than four hours' notice and, if cornered by a hostile question, would turn upon the questioner for being 'susceptible to Jewish-Communist propaganda'.

One of his main assistants for briefing the lobby was Sir Joseph Ball, a shadowy figure recruited from MI5 to run the Conservatives' own intelligence service. He did so using many of the techniques he had learned from his former employer. The phones of Anthony Eden and his fellow anti-appeasers were tapped and the names of other fellow Conservatives were blackened through a periodical ironically called *Truth*. This supposedly independent publication had been secretly acquired by friends of Chamberlain to act as the mouthpiece for his faction within the Conservative party. Under this ownership, it became viciously anti-Churchill, anti-Semitic, anti-American and pacifist.

Members of Chamberlain's Cabinet circle were on close personal terms with most of the big newspaper proprietors and editors of the day. In the case of the relationship between Chamberlain and Geoffrey Dawson, the editor of *The Times*, the links were so close that *The Times* became regarded as the unofficial voice of the British government, and was closely studied for that reason in government offices throughout the world.

But none of the relationships was on quite the same basis as that between Lord Beaverbrook and Sir Samuel Hoare (Lord Privy Seal in the Chamberlain War Cabinet). From 1938 Hoare was receiving secret payments of £2,000 per year from Beaverbrook, and in return lobbied for Beaverbrook to be given a Cabinet position, as Minister of Agriculture.

Another close and improper relationship was that between George Steward, Chamberlain's Press Officer and Dr Hesse, the Press Attaché at the German Embassy. Through Steward, Hesse was able to learn the true attribution of stories reported through the lobby system, and was thus able to gauge the true tenor of British government opinion in the tense negotiations on either side of the Munich agreement. Steward's relationship with Hesse has variously been described as 'strictly against his code of conduct as a civil servant' and 'treasonable'.

The British Ambassador to Berlin was Sir Nevile Henderson. He was an extreme appeaser – when the English football team played in Berlin in May 1938 he insisted that they all gave the Nazi salute, and he told a gathering of the Anglo-German Society: 'Far too many people have an erroneous conception about what the National-Socialist regime really stands for. Otherwise they would lay much less stress on Nazi dictatorship and much more emphasis on the great social experiment being tried out in this country.' Henderson very quickly picked up upon Hitler's extreme and irrational sensitivity to criticism in the British press. This message was also drummed into Lord Halifax, by Goebbels and by Hitler himself during Halifax's visit to Germany in November 1937. It was made clear to Halifax that progress on a peace settlement was dependent upon suppression of the criticism of Hitler in the British press.

Chamberlain and his colleagues duly complied by exerting pressure on newspaper owners and editors alike. Some journalists bitterly resented this regime. As J.L. Garvin, the editor of the *Observer*, put it in August 1938:

'The daily press no longer gives any true idea of the feeling of this country. There is at last – wide anxiety – a slow, eating anxiety, though silent and feeling helpless. There is not one particle of sympathy any more with Germany.' His proprietor, Lord Astor, voiced similar concerns, '. . . although the newspapers might have been silenced now . . . there was widespread uneasiness and that was likely to show itself soon'.

Questions were asked in Parliament about the muzzling of the press. First Halifax equivocated, then Chamberlain openly lied to the Commons about whether government influence was being exercised over the newspapers. But Chamberlain's hand was evident in the notorious *Times* editorial of 7 September 1938, in which it openly advocated the dismemberment of Czechoslovakia. Both Jan Masaryk, the Czech Minister to London, and his Russian counterpart, protested to the Foreign Office. As Masaryk put it, the Foreign Office's belief in the independence of *The Times* 'is not shared by a very large section of the population abroad'.

> Colonel Blimp explains:
> 'Gad sir, *The Times* is right!
> We should give
> Czechoslovakia a free
> hand in Europe.'

Beaverbrook was among the most acquiescent of the press barons. He told the government that, while the press were totally behind them, they needed a lot more guidance. A minister should be appointed to brief them directly. The minister he suggested was Sir Samuel Hoare. The proposal was accepted, and Hoare – the man on Beaverbrook's payroll – was soon dispensing daily briefings to the British press. Some journalists, frustrated by the line dictated by their employers, found an independent voice in private publications such as the *Whitehall News Letter*, which attacked Chamberlain and his entourage. By the early months of the war, these publications had a combined circulation of around 100,000.

During this period, the government sought to extend its control over public expression beyond the newspapers. The Lord Chamberlain, who at that time exercised powers to censor plays, was asked by the Foreign Office to ensure that: 'All direct references to Germany, to Herr Hitler, or to other prominent persons should be avoided . . . since they would be . . . not only dangerous, but unnecessary.' They also drew the attention of the British Board of Film Censors to a forthcoming Charlie Chaplin film, *The Great Dictator*, which they described as 'a bitter and ridiculous . . . satire which Mr Chaplin is entering into with fanatical enthusiasm', and urged the Censors 'to give the film the most careful scrutiny should it be presented to you for a licence'.

The film was only eventually released in 1940. The BBC also came under scrutiny. Its compliance had been thought for a number of years to have been guaranteed by its dependence on the government for the licence fee. However, from the mid-1930s its coverage of current affairs was watched closely by the government, resulting in what the Chief News Editor referred to as a 'conspiracy of silence'. In one example, a talk by Harold Nicolson on the Czechoslovak crisis was withdrawn at the insistence of the Foreign Secretary, and the sound engineer stood ready to fade Nicolson out, should he depart from the content of his innocuous alternative script.

Perhaps most outrageously of all, just before the invasion of Czechoslovakia, *Truth* ran a nauseating feature on 'Hitler the artist', waxing lyrical about his watercolours and the warm, human and sensitive man they portrayed. Was it, they wondered, 'possible that the real Hitler, the genuine little Adolf, is a sensitive child, intensely occupied with his own shy moods?'

Only in the very last days of peace did the press finally begin to reflect the mood of the nation. Hoare's final desperate attempts to bully the press into compliance with continued appeasement in late August fell upon deaf ears.

The press would pay a high price, in terms of public trust, for its spinelessness. A Mass Observation survey in March 1940 showed that the public now only ranked it third in its list of opinion-formers. Two years before, it had been first. Another survey in August 1940 found that, by a majority of more than three to one, the public now found the BBC a more reliable source of news than the press. The circulations of the main pro-Chamberlain newspapers fell sharply, while those few which had consistently opposed him – such as the *Daily Mirror* – enjoyed a correspondingly rapid rise. The newspaper industry would never fully regain the trust it had enjoyed before Chamberlain.

From the moment he was restored to government as First Lord of the Admiralty, Winston Churchill made it clear that he was also adept in manipulating the media (and not above manipulating the facts, if they stood in the way of the message he wanted to convey). The Navy already had the most effective of the forces' media organisations, and Churchill milked it shamelessly to his own ends. Good news stories were suppressed until he could announce them in his own speeches. Vice-Admiral Hallett from the Admiralty Press Office made the unpardonable error of releasing some of these stories himself. He rapidly found himself removed from the press office and posted out to sea. Churchill said in one speech that it was 'pretty certain' that about half the U-boat fleet had been sunk. When naval intelligence told him that the true figure was no higher than 9 out of 66, Churchill simply replied that 35 was 'the lowest figure that can be accepted'.

WAR MEANS NEVER HAVING TO SAY YOU'RE SORRY

Along with direct censorship, journalistic euphemisms for wartime reverses became commonplace. A rout became 'a retrograde movement', a 'disengagement' or simply 'straightening the line'. Insanity caused by prolonged exposure to fighting became 'battle fatigue' or 'exhaustion'. The V1 flying bombs became known as the cosy 'doodlebugs', and their successors the V2s (which arrived at such a speed that they could not even be heard coming, let alone shot down) were initially blamed on gas explosions. Cynics christened them 'flying gas mains'. The sites where they landed were 'incidents'.

Even sceptical members of the armed forces got in on the euphemism act. Bomber crews participating in a raid on a German city that spectacularly failed to find its target spoke of 'a major assault on German agriculture'. However, the prize for the finest euphemism of the war must go to Emperor Hirohito of Japan. After the two atomic bombs had fallen on Hiroshima and Nagasaki, the Emperor made a radio broadcast to the nation in which he told them that they were surrendering because: 'The war has taken a turn not necessarily to our advantage.'

THE MYSTERY OF INFORMATION

I may say that I have had considerable difficulty in ascertaining what are its functions.

Lord Macmillan, Minister of Information.

It was a perfectly useless body and the war would have been in no way affected if it had been dissolved and only the censorship remained.

Sir Kenneth Clark, Controller of Home Publicity in the Ministry of Information.

The Ministry of Information is a misbegotten freak bred from the unnatural union of Sir Horace Wilson and Sir Samuel Hoare (considering the progenitors, I wonder the offspring is not even more revolting).

Duff Cooper, Minister of Information.

If the Germans do not manage to bomb us to death the Ministry of Information will bore us to death.

Aneurin Bevan.

Hush, hush, chuckle who dares,
Another new Minister's fallen downstairs.

Popular rhyme at the Ministry, reflecting its rapid changes of Minister.

It takes a special talent for the organisation in charge of wartime propaganda itself to become widely unpopular and the butt of jokes, but that is what the Ministry of Information contrived to do. Frequently referred to as the Ministry for Misinformation or the Mystery of Information, when it announced that it had 999 members of staff – the same as the telephone number for the emergency services – it promptly also became known as The Disaster Department.

The Ministry of Information was planned from 1935 to 'present the national case to the public at home and abroad in time of war'. It was finally set up in 1939, and Goebbels' Ministry of Propaganda was influential in shaping its form and function. It was granted swingeing powers under the Emergency Powers (Defence) Act, to censor not just information of value to the enemy but also opinion hostile to the government and anti-war sentiment. This, and its lion's share of scarce wartime paper supplies, helped to earn it the immediate jealousy and hostility of the media.

The Ministry suffered badly from the rapid turnover of its ministers. *Time* magazine said of its first minister, the High Court Judge Lord Macmillan: 'If Lord Macmillan's first task was to undo Britain's reputation for cleverness, he could not have done it more brilliantly.' His successors, Sir John Reith and Duff Cooper, fared little better. Reith was sacked by Churchill as part of a long-running vendetta, immediately he became prime minister, and Cooper, who was described by Ponting as a 'reactionary womaniser' who was both incompetent and lazy, saw his political career ended by his failure there. It was only under Brendan Bracken that the Ministry shook off its reputation as an incompetent joke and began to perform a useful function. The recruitment of its more junior staff was no happier. It was mostly done through the old boy network, making it a hotbed of amateurism (only 43 of the 999 staff were trained journalists). The *New Statesman* referred to a 'scramble of socially favoured amateurs and privileged ignoramuses into the Ministry of Information'.

One of its leading lights, the MP Harold Nicolson, was described by a colleague as: 'a wonderful gossip but [he] seemed to know hardly anyone outside Westminster, St James and Bloomsbury. He was quite ignorant of the habits and attitudes even of the middle classes. . . . Never was there a man who represented so completely in himself the distinction between us and them.'

Originally, the Ministry was a bold idea for centralising the processing of all government information and propaganda. However, vested interests ensured that the idea got watered down in practice, and individual departmental press offices survived. The inexperience of the staff soon brought them into disrepute. Their censorship was inadequate and inconsistent and they were held responsible for the lack of news reaching the press – a charge which should more properly have been laid at the door of the press organisations of the individual government departments and armed services. The fact that only four prosecutions were carried out during the war under the censorship regulations says less about the responsible behaviour of the newspapers, and more about the difficulty the papers had tracking down any news 'hot' enough to infringe the regulations. The Ministry's accreditation of overseas war correspondents in Britain was so strict that about a hundred of them decamped for Berlin, where it was rather easier to get reliable information.

The lack of news in the early part of the war was held to be partly responsible for the proliferation of rumours (for example, that the royal family or the government were about to flee to Canada, or that the Duke of Windsor was to be appointed leader of a puppet administration). This led in turn to the establishment of the Ministry's Anti-Lies Bureau and to the doomed Silent Column campaign, referred to below.

Their coverage of the departure of the British Expeditionary Force to France illustrates their incompetence in dealing with the media. Initially, they banned the news, until they found it was being broadcast by the French. They then lifted the ban, and newspaper editors rushed it into their editions. The Ministry then decided that the media were giving too many details of the action and re-imposed the ban. The police were brought in to confiscate copies of the morning papers from newsagents and other suppliers. Finally, at 2.55 a.m., the ban was lifted for a second time, leaving newspaper editors to bite the carpet with rage.

Other aspects of the MOI's early handling of public relations were incompetent to a point that beggars belief. When war correspondent John Gunther asked for the text of some of the eighteen million leaflets that RAF bombers dropped on Germany, he was refused on the remarkable grounds that it was 'information which could be of value to the enemy'. This gave rise to a rich vein of speculation about the leaflets – that they were inaccurate, out-of-date or full of spelling mistakes. Best of all, some said that the Ministry had got the packages mixed up and had dropped a supply of our ration books on the Germans instead. In fact, a good proportion of the leaflets consisted of extracts from speeches by Neville Chamberlain and Lord Halifax. As Noel Coward, who was peripherally involved with this aspect of wartime propaganda at one time, put it: 'If it is the policy of H.M. Government to bore the Germans to death, I do not believe we have quite enough time.'

> Colonel Blimp explains: 'Gad sir, Mr Baldwin is right! To ensure peace, we must have plenty of aeroplanes. Otherwise how are we going to drop messages of goodwill on the enemy?'

The Ministry's first poster campaign proved disastrous in stoking up the fires of class conflict that were still smouldering from pre-war society. It said: '*Your* courage, *your* cheerfulness, *your* resolution will bring *us* victory.'

A survey by the *Daily Express* showed that 33 per cent of the women questioned and 11 per cent of the men had not even noticed the posters (plastered everywhere, at the considerable cost of £44,000). A significant proportion of those who had seen them apparently did not understand them (many thought that the 'resolution' referred to was the New Year's variety). But 61 per cent of the men surveyed who had seen and understood it took exception to it. For, to those who chose to read it in such a light, the slogan meant that 'you' (the poor bloody infantry of the working classes) will make all the sacrifices that will give 'us' (the establishment) the spoils of victory. Just to complete the Ministry's success, anti-Semites began to exploit the fascist potential of the poster, and went round doctoring them to read '. . . will bring *Jew* victory'. It was rapidly dropped. No more successful was their 'Silent Column' campaign, launched in July 1940. The aim of this was to stop people spreading rumour and gossip, alarm and despondency. Unfortunately, it did so using characters with names like Mr Know-All, Miss Leaky Mouth and Mr Glumpot, and was written in language that was no less patronising than the names. Worst of all, it tried to turn Britain into a nation of snoopers, inviting them to inform on any transgressors.

Some did; drunks and the feeble-minded were arrested, and one soldier in a Soho pub was imprisoned for shouting 'To hell with Hitler!', when it was misheard as 'Heil Hitler!' A woman, overcome by a moment of careless rapture in a hotel bedroom, blurted out to her boyfriend: 'Who cares if Hitler does come, so long as we can have fun like this!' She was overheard by a hotel chambermaid and received a month in prison.

The newspaper advertisements lasted just three weeks, before Churchill was forced to admit in Parliament that the campaign did not look so attractive on paper as it had seemed in prospect. Dorothy L. Sayers, writing in the *Spectator*, showed how badly it had misread the mood of the nation:

Nobody said that if Mr Churchill had put it on paper himself it would have looked very different. Mr Churchill knows how to be more insolently offensive than any man living, but he exercises his unique abilities in this direction against the enemy, not against his own people. He never suggests to us that we are a bunch of fools and cowards who need to be incessantly scolded into resolution. . . .

. . . We have been shown a very faint glimpse of the thing that we are fighting against, and now that we have seen it, we know for certain that we hate it beyond all imagination. To distrust our fellows, to become spies on them, to betray them to the law, to go in a continual dumb terror for fear they should spy on us – that is the thing that Nazi government means, and it is a thing we will not endure.

Home Intelligence reports also picked up the public sentiment:

Strong resentment still felt among all classes at Silent Column campaign and at police prosecutions for spreading rumour, which are considered ridiculous. Ministry of Information becoming unpopular again; much of this feeling directed against the Minister. Indignation expressed at what people say to be 'a policy which is turning us into a nation of spies'. Labour Party candidates' meeting agreed that prosecutions for idle talking were upsetting public morale seriously. People in new positions of minor authority accused of officiousness and bullying manner, reminiscent, some say 'of the early days of the Nazis'.

The Silent Column campaign possibly marked the nadir of the Ministry's reputation, but it was by no means their last mistake. Mass Observation pilot-tested their 'Stay Put' leaflet, designed to prevent the public panicking and fleeing their homes in the event of an invasion. They found that the public were highly critical of its schoolmasterly tone and disapproved of the leaflet in a ratio of 3:1.

Sometimes it was the Ministry's timing that was off. In the middle of 1940 they issued a 32-page brochure, talking about there having been 'six months without any serious fighting on land'. It came out just as the British Expeditionary Force was engaging in some very serious fighting indeed, on the road back to Dunkirk. The Ministry also managed to upset the film-going public. The Ministry took over the highly regarded GPO Film Unit in April 1940 and turned it into the propaganda film-making wing of their operations. It was given the first call on scarce film stock, above the feature films the public really wanted to see, and cinemas were forced to show their propaganda short features. They were not popular with the public, who were generally cynical about them and resented having to sit through them to get to the feature they had actually paid to watch.

On one occasion the Ministry actually wanted to raise the blood pressure of the British public. There was a feeling in 1940 that the public lacked sufficient hostility to the Germans. The Ministry proposed an 'Anger Campaign', invoking the same kind of crude propaganda that had been used in the First World War (Huns bayoneting babies and Belgian nuns). This failed to recognise the cynicism which had been engendered in the public when that propaganda had subsequently been found to be untrue. This cynicism was said to be why some of the public failed at first to believe the stories of the Nazi concentration camps, when they began to emerge. The Ministry withheld some of these early stories, owing to concerns about anti-Semitism among the public at the time. The Ministry also suggested that: 'A few death sentences on traitors would have a great effect in heightening the public temper against the enemy.'

The Anger Campaign was never implemented on the scale – or with some of the wilder ideas – proposed by the Ministry.

PROPAGANDA – CATCH THEM YOUNG

It was not just the hearts and minds of the adult population that were being won over to the war effort. The youngsters had their own diet of propaganda. As George Orwell recalled, the more traditional boys' papers, such as the *Gem* and the *Magnet*, were still stuck in an imperialistic time warp, from about 1910, in which Nazism had failed to make even an appearance by the end of September 1939. Arthur Mee's *Children's Newspaper* took a traditional patriotic line, producing a series of articles on *1940: Our Finest Hour*. However, brash newcomers like the *Beano* and the *Dandy* were most definitely at war. In them, Hitler and Goering were portrayed as Addy and Hermy, the Nasty Nazis. They would watch the British Isles through their magic telescope and reel back in horror, crying 'Himmel! Der pig-dog British are saving all their waste paper!'

Mussolini was Musso da Wop ('he's a bit of a flop') and no national stereotype was spared in the attempt to pour ridicule on him – even to the extent of his generals issuing their troops with spaghetti for bootlaces. (A contemporary riddle: 'Why does Mussolini never change his socks? Because he smells defeat'.) In its stablemate, the *Dandy Comic Annual* for 1941, Desperate Dan can be seen capturing three U-boats single-handedly, with a chain he has just knitted. 'Frizzle mein Aunt von Fanny!' cries a German submariner; 'Danny der Desperate has our goose cooked!' For the more literate consumer of comics, *Champion* had characters such as Rockfist Rogan of the RAF and The Leader of the Lost Commandos, while those of a more traditional bent could enjoy Struewwelhitler or Adolf in Blunderland, parodies of the classic children's stories.

There were children's games based on every aspect of the war – you could play Bomber Command, Air Sea Rescue, River Plate, ARP or Hang Your Washing on the Siegfried Line. Pin the Tail on the Donkey was given a new look as Decorate Goering, and darts games featuring Hitler were popular. In Plonk, you scored 100 for a dart in the Führer's mouth. (Another game (perhaps fortunately un-named) scored top marks for hitting quite the opposite end of his alimentary canal.)

Many historians would identify the entry of Russia or America into the war as turning points in the conflict, but comic readers everywhere will confirm that the Axis powers stood no chance from the moment that they took on both Desperate Dan and Lord Snooty and his Pals.

CENSORSHIP

The possibility of introducing total press censorship was seriously considered by the wartime government, but it was felt to sit too uneasily with their self-appointed role as guardians of civil liberties in the world. Similarly, there was talk of making the BBC a department of government, but this again would have compromised its façade of independence with its world audience. Instead, they appointed civil servants as 'advisers', who in fact had powers of total direction over the Corporation's news output.

The judgement of the Ministry as to what the public should or should not be told was continually found to be faulty. After the bombing of Buckingham Palace, they busily set about suppressing all news of it. Churchill was reported to have responded as follows: 'Dolts! Idiots! Fools! Spread the news at once! Let it be broadcast everywhere. Let the people of London know that the King and Queen are sharing the perils with them.' Or, as A.J.P. Taylor put it: 'There was a difference between the King and his subjects. They had essential work to do, he could have gone through his "boxes" just as well at Windsor. He attended at Buckingham Palace solely to be bombed.'

When Noel Coward proposed making a film based on the sinking of Lord Louis Mountbatten's ship HMS *Kelly* during the battle for Crete, the Ministry initially banned it, on the grounds that a film showing a British ship sinking would be bad for morale. It was only after Mountbatten intervened through the person of King George VI himself that the ban was lifted. *In Which We Serve* went on to be probably Britain's most successful wartime film, winning Coward a special Oscar for his 'outstanding production achievement'.

Coward was once again a victim of the Ministry's censorship with his cabaret song 'Don't let's be beastly to the Germans'. The irony of the song went entirely over the heads of the civil servants, who banned it from being recorded or broadcast on the grounds that Goebbels might use some of its words for propaganda purposes. This was despite the fact that Coward had played it to Winston Churchill, to the latter's obvious amusement.

Another of the Ministry's ill-judged forays into artistic censorship was in relation to Colonel Blimp. The Colonel, created by *Evening Standard* cartoonist David Low in 1934, was a bigoted, incompetent and reactionary former military man, whose collected thoughts appear at various points in this book and whose name entered the language. George Orwell, for example, described the Home Guard as 'a people's army, officered by Blimps'. When Michael Powell announced in 1942 that he was to make a film based on the character, Churchill wrote to the Minister for Information, Brendan Bracken, in the following Blimpish terms:

Pray propose to me the measures necessary to stop this foolish production before it gets any further. I am not prepared to allow propaganda detrimental to the morale of the army and I am sure the Cabinet will take all necessary action. Who are the people behind it?

The Ministry vetted the script and eventually approved it. Quite how great their impact was is not known, but the character that emerged in *The Life and Death of Colonel Blimp* was a much more sympathetic figure, a decent and honourable man who had simply lived beyond his time – 'a lovable old walrus', as one film critic put it. The film was a huge success, helped not a little by Churchill's attempts at censorship, but Churchill none the less still tried to have its export banned. For years afterwards, the only print available of it was a heavily edited version.

Attempts by the Ministry to organise a wartime social survey earned the organisation the new nickname Cooper's Snoopers, after its then Minister, Duff Cooper. People interpreted their no-doubt well-meaning efforts to find out what was on the nation's minds as a sinister attempt to manipulate public opinion, though very few of the public declined to take part in it.

Radio broadcasts were subject to strict controls. J.B. Priestley's radio broadcasts during the early years of the war were second in popularity only to those of Churchill himself, but he made the mistake of suggesting that the war might be about something beyond just beating Hitler. His discussion of the better world that the nation might aspire to after the war earned him a number of powerful enemies. The Conservative 1922 Committee lobbied the Ministry of Information, and Churchill complained that Priestley's war aims conflicted with his own. David Margesson, the government Chief Whip, objected to the BBC about the leftward slant of Priestley's talks (which, given that Margesson was supposed to be part of a coalition government including socialists, may seem like an abuse of his position). Eventually, a terse memorandum went to a BBC Board meeting in March 1941: 'Priestley series stopping on instructions of Minister.'

The Ministry had the power to vet scripts and approve speakers. Even then, their representative sat in Broadcasting House, ready to fade out any broadcaster who might dare to depart from the approved text (an extension of the practice employed in a more limited way before the war by Chamberlain's government). The Ministry's deference to its traditional audiences – the newspapers – also used to rebound on the BBC on occasion. They would embargo the release of important news in evening broadcasts in order to give the scoop to the morning papers. This meant, for example, that details of a Cabinet reshuffle were made public on foreign radio stations before the BBC was allowed to broadcast them.

Nothing was too innocuous to cause the authorities to take fright. Wartime radio listeners derived much innocent pleasure from listening to a radio programme called *The Brains Trust*. In this, a panel consisting of a dangerously subversive mixture of the Secretary of the London Zoological Society, a teacher of philosophy and a retired Royal Navy commander answered listeners' questions about anything under the sun. Pompous members of the Establishment began to complain about the undermining of their position as the repository of all wisdom by this programme, and the BBC duly started to vet all the questions. The absence of a member of the Established Church on the panel led them to ban questions about religion, and even to run an edition of the programme with a panel entirely composed of churchmen (not a great success). Then, any questions that might embarrass the government, such as 'should there be equal pay for men and women?' were banned. Finally, the BBC governors decided that the three individuals concerned were becoming too influential, and banned them from appearing together on the programme. Each was limited to just one appearance every three weeks.

Censorship did not even stop at words. Once Russia entered the war, Churchill was very concerned that this would promote the cause of Communism in Britain. He told the Ministry of Information to 'consider what action is required to counter the present tendency of the British public to forget the dangers of Communism in their enthusiasm over the resistance of Russia'.

One of the more ludicrous manifestations of this policy was in relation to the Russian national anthem, the 'Internationale'. Churchill issued an instruction that it was on no account to be played by the BBC. The BBC at this time had a programme on which they played the national anthems of all the Allied nations. Once Russia joined the Allied cause, they resolutely resisted all demands from the public to play the 'Internationale' on this programme, eventually scrapping the programme rather than yield to the pressure. Only in January 1942, and with great reluctance, was Churchill persuaded by Anthony Eden to drop his ban on the anthem, in the light of all the negative publicity it was attracting. More generally, there was a ban on playing the music of composers from Axis nations – not for any ideological reason, but for the more practical purpose of avoiding paying royalties to enemy nationals.

In another bizarre example of gratuitous censorship, the BBC cancelled a Christmas choral concert in 1940, which was due to be conducted by Sir Hugh Robertson. This was because Robertson was a pacifist who was privately critical of the government, who presumably might therefore conduct the carols in an unsuitably pacifist manner and thus promote defeatism. The Ministry of Information developed a reputation as a sanctuary for draft-dodging failed hacks and other

A LETTER FROM THE CENSOR

From the very start of the war, there was censorship of correspondence. A small army of over ten thousand civil servants worked in a network of offices around the country, checking letters, telegrams, books and news agency reports coming into or going out of the country. They checked not just for information that could be of value to the enemy, but also for anything defeatist, or which might bring the Allied war effort into disrepute. As the threat of invasion grew in 1940, this was extended to include internal correspondence within the British Isles. Quite how widely this latter power was used is not known, though it is thought to have been directed primarily at known or suspected dissidents. In addition, the authorities also had the power to eavesdrop on private telephone conversations.

would-be literary spirits, and was savagely lampooned in Evelyn Waugh's 1942 book *Put out more flags*. One other literary connection with the government's wartime propaganda efforts was the book *1984*. George Orwell's first wife was involved with the propaganda work of the Ministry of Food, and it is thought that some of the sloganising in that book (not to mention the perennial complaints about shortages) was based upon her experience.

In the interest of balance, it has to be said that some of the Ministry's other campaigns, such as 'Careless talk costs lives' and 'Walls have ears' were so successful that they helped to fuel the paranoia about a ubiquitous Fifth Column, discussed elsewhere in this book.

NEWSPAPER CENSORSHIP

Newspaper censorship could lead to some ludicrous anomalies. Papers could report on which German cities had been attacked by the RAF, but a raid which destroyed, for example, a substantial part of the centre of Reading could only be described for weeks afterwards in the town's newspaper as taking place in 'a home counties town' (as if the local population might not have spotted it). Even Manchester's air raids in December 1940, which left 1,000 people dead, 75,000 houses damaged and 37,000 people homeless, could not be pinpointed by the media any more specifically than 'an inland town in the north west'. The weather was also forbidden as a topic for the newspapers, on the grounds that it might aid and abet German bombers.

Any questioning of the conduct of the war soon attracted the wrath of the censors. While the Russian-German non-aggression pact lasted, the Communist *Daily Worker* was firmly anti-war, leading to its suppression by the government. Of the mainstream newspapers, the *Daily Mirror* was just about the only one seriously to question government conduct of the war. This was despite the fact that the paper had been strongly pro-Churchill during the Chamberlain administration, and had even asked Churchill to write for them.

A cartoon of a shipwrecked seaman, clinging on to some wreckage in the water, above a caption 'The price of petrol has been increased by one penny' led to threats of the paper being suppressed. The offending cartoon was supposed to illustrate the hardships endured by seamen to supply us with petrol, and the consequent need to conserve supplies, but the government misinterpreted it to be conveying some morale-sapping message about profiteering. Churchill himself was quite vituperative about the independence shown by the *Daily Mirror*. As he wrote to the proprietor, Cecil King: 'There is a spirit of hatred and malice against the government which surpasses anything I have ever seen in English journalism. One would have thought that in these hard times some hatred might be kept for the enemy.'

Churchill's malice towards King and the *Mirror* even extended to trying to get King conscripted (he failed the medical) and having the intelligence services investigate the share ownership of the paper for evidence of subversive influences. Despite his own background as a journalist, Churchill treated the press with a similar contempt to that shown by Neville Chamberlain. He was one of the leading protagonists for tighter control over the media and even objected to factual reports of speeches by MPs critical of the government – the Ministry would censor the offending passages. Home Intelligence never uncovered any evidence that the independence of the press – such as it was – damaged morale. On the contrary, the safety valve it provided very probably had quite the opposite effect. It certainly appeared to be what the public wanted – the *Daily Mirror* enjoyed a massive rise in circulation during the war years, in contrast to some of its more compliant rivals.

With the outbreak of war, Beaverbrook's papers switched from being arch-appeasers to being arch-complainers about a war that they saw as unnecessary and avoidable. The *Express* ran campaigns against rationing, the blackout and other aspects of wartime regulation. In October 1939 the *Sunday Express* published a defeatist interview with Lloyd George, in which the former prime minister declared that Poland was not worth fighting for. But Beaverbrook's anti-war efforts, prior to his 'rehabilitation' under Winston Churchill, were not limited to editorial matters. He also attempted to get the Duke of Windsor to front a peace campaign, and sought to fund the anti-war Independent Labour Party. In fact, Beaverbrook was not at all fussy about the company he kept; he also assiduously courted the favours of Stalin, once the Russians had entered the war.

Truth magazine continued throughout the war. Sir Joseph Ball's fanatical loyalty to Chamberlain continued after the latter's death, with Ball using the magazine to attack the enemies of the Chamberlain camp, such as Eden and Churchill, even after they became members of the wartime government. He conducted a particularly unpleasant anti-Semitic campaign against Leslie Hore-Belisha, after his resignation from the Chamberlain Cabinet in January 1940. If anything, the magazine's pro-fascist tendencies grew more pronounced in wartime. At one stage, they had Major-General Fuller (Sir Oswald Mosley's one-time adviser on military affairs) writing a piece denying the existence of German concentration camps.

When British fascist sympathisers were rounded up under Regulation 18B, *Truth* championed the cause of these internees. The most disturbing aspect of this was that Ball was at the same time the Vice-Chairman of the so-called Swinton Committee, which was supposed to be responsible for rounding up the fascists. *Truth*'s fascist sympathies led to calls in Parliament in 1941 for the magazine to be suppressed. Ball and fellow director Charles Crocker – also on the Swinton Committee – were forced to disentangle themselves from *Truth* rather rapidly. When Ball finally finished at the Conservative Research Department, all its records were found to have been destroyed.

BROADCASTING

The lack of imagination of some of the BBC's broadcasting efforts in the early part of the war (they seemed to consist largely of Sandy Macpherson and the BBC theatre organ) made it easy for German propagandists to attract British listeners. They launched a number of stations, purporting to be dissident British broadcasters and thereby helping to foster the idea of an active Fifth Column within Britain. The first of these, the New British Broadcasting Station, went on the air on 25 February 1940, and was followed by Workers' Challenge, Caledonia and the Christian Peace Movement, appealing variously to class, nationalist and pacifist sentiments.

As long as there was little real news for the BBC to report, these stations (whose frequencies were published in the daily newspapers) attracted a good proportion of the British listening public. The Ministry of Information estimated in January 1940 that 26 per cent of the population had listened in the previous twenty-four hours to their most famous propagandist, William Joyce. Another survey suggested that no fewer than 24 million British people listened to him at least occasionally. The BBC was even forced into a ratings war, moving some of its most popular programmes around to try to win listeners back from the Germans. As one listener put it to Mass Observation: 'We nearly always turn him [Lord Haw-Haw] on at nine fifteen to try and glean some news that the Ministry of Information withholds from us.'

More worryingly, another survey showed that 17 per cent agreed with Joyce's assessment that the war was being conducted for the benefit of an international Jewish conspiracy. The *Daily Mirror* set up an 'Anti-Haw-Haw League of Loyal Britons', who vowed never to listen to, or even mention, the man. Mention of Haw-Haw could, in fact, be dangerous. A civil servant from Mansfield was prosecuted for inventing a Haw-Haw story about the schools in his area, as was a Birmingham businessman for telling his staff that Haw-Haw broadcast news of a fire before it was generally known about even in Britain.

BLACK PROPAGANDA

Both sides made use of misleading or salacious propaganda, in an effort to demoralise the enemy. On the British side, efforts were co-ordinated by the Political Warfare Executive, which was established in August 1941. Like the Germans, they broadcast radio programmes purporting to be produced by dissidents within the enemy state itself. The content of the programmes was decided by Sefton Delmer, the German-born son of an Australian father and British mother, who produced a potent mixture of popular music and often-pornographic scandal about the sexual peccadilloes of the Nazi establishment. The station was called GS1 and Delmer broadcast in the character of 'Der Chef', an uncompromising, patriotic Prussian. So salacious were his reports that even the German High Command complained about his 'quite unusually wicked hate propaganda'.

Even our own side protested – one broadcast in the summer of 1942, describing an orgy involving high Nazi officials, was picked up in Moscow. It outraged the sober and humourless former British Ambassador there, Sir Stafford Cripps, who demanded that they be toned down. Delmer's chief responded robustly:

> If the Secret Service were to be too squeamish, the Secret Service could not operate
> . . . this is a war with the gloves off, and when I was asked to deal with black
> propaganda I did not try to restrain my people more than M [the Head of the
> Secret Service] would restrain his, because if you are told to fight you fight all out.
> I am not conscious that it has depraved me. I dislike the baser sides of human life
> as much as Sir Stafford Cripps does, but in this case moral indignation does not
> seem to be called for.

Delmer was none the less told to tone down the pornographic content of his scripts. In addition to GS1, there were specialised stations, such as Atlantiksender, for U-boat crews, and Soldatensenders, for German land troops in Europe. These might carry stories about Nazi officials' sex scandals with the wives of absent troops; news that much of the blood in German field hospitals was infected with syphilis; or details of married women giving birth to babies at a time when their husbands had been absent at the front for over a year.

Anything that might foster disaffection among the troops was tried: the army pay corps were stealing their pay; their parcels from home were being pilfered; the jobs they hoped to return to after the war were now being filled on a permanent basis by homosexuals and those declared unfit for military service; Gauleiters were stealing the personal effects of dead German soldiers. They mixed speculation with facts, gleaned from captured German personnel or Enigma transcripts. Not even astrological forecasts were too improbable to be pressed into service.

In retrospect, the black propaganda of both sides probably had less effect generally upon the war than on the peace which followed. The broadcasts were probably not widely believed and their entertainment content was such that they probably increased morale, rather than reducing it. The Germans took them seriously enough, however, and Goebbels felt no compunction in crying 'foul' at some of the British efforts at black propaganda: 'Whenever our High Command must keep silent about the operations on the front for military reasons, British propaganda is busy to create unrest among Germans.'

For those Germans who engaged in rumour-mongering, based on these broadcasts, he had the sternest of warnings: 'Such behaviour is not only criminal but is also utterly unfair to the soldiers who suffer such hardships on the front and to the Führer and his commanders who prepare the way to victory. Such rumour-mongers deserve death. Two have already been executed. . . .'

The British took an altogether more gentlemanly approach to the matter, as this Ministry of Information advertisement shows:

> What do I do if I come across German or Italian broadcasts when tuning my wireless? I say to myself: 'Now this blighter wants me to listen to him. Am I going to do what he wants? I remember that German lies over the air are like parachute troops dropping on Britain – they are part of the plan to get us down – which they won't. I just remember nobody can trust a word the Haw Haws say. So, just to make them waste their time, I switch 'em off or tune 'em out.

One, more lasting, effect of these broadcasts may have been to increase the threshold of tolerance to sexual transgressions, and thus pave the way, twenty years later, for the permissive society of the 1960s.

> THE CENSOR CALLS. . . .
>
> The zeal of mail censors could be misplaced, often along with their sense of humour. A woman in Eire sent her daughter in England some eggs. The latter sent a letter of thanks, in which she jokingly remarked 'I wish you would send me a cow!' The letter was duly returned by the censor with the following words added: 'Import of cattle into England from Eire by private individuals is not permitted. This letter, therefore, which asks for a prohibited article, is returned to sender.'

CARELESS TALK

The first days of the war led to entire British towns being destroyed by bombing, including, in some cases, attacks from Zeppelins, and the first case of a German gas attack – or at least it did according to the fertile imaginations of rumour-mongers up and down the country. The bombing raids were, of course, pure fiction, while the gas attack that somebody smelt was in fact a fire in a Southampton pickle factory.

The Ministry of Information tried, throughout the war and with varying degrees of success, to stem the flow of rumours. One explanation for their proliferation (and for the initial high audience figures for the official German rumour-monger, Lord Haw-Haw) was that the public did not believe what they were being told by the official media. Mass Observation reported that, in the early weeks of the war, people said it was useless to buy newspapers since all the front pages were identical and could not be trusted. Lack of anything happening on the war front was taken as evidence that we were not being told the truth. Another reason given for spreading rumours was that they helped to spice up the boredom that was a central part of wartime life.

Rumours in wartime take on many and varied forms – troops evacuated from Dunkirk who left their kit behind would have it docked from their pay; the London park railings, sawn down for the war effort, had been found to be useless and secretly dumped off Portsmouth; further afield, the Japanese broadcaster Tokyo Rose was in fact the missing aviator Amelia Earhart, captured in the Pacific and brainwashed; a dog was found, near Pearl Harbor after the raid, barking in morse code to an offshore submarine.

Some rumours had positive propaganda functions. The suggestion that carrots helped you see in the dark not only encouraged a healthy diet (not to mention one that was not in short supply); it was also used to account for the success of our night-fighter pilots and disguise the success of radar (or was this another rumour?) Another was that Lord Woolton's national wholemeal loaf had remarkable aphrodisiac qualities. (Ernest Bevin, for one, was not seduced by this – he claimed this unpopular bread was inedible and gave him wind.)

But there was more than mere disapproval for rumour-mongering. Douglas Sunderland of Cokington, Derbyshire, got three months in gaol for handing round a propaganda leaflet dropped by the Luftwaffe. Relaying simple information could be classed as spreading alarm and despondency and would get you into trouble. Maidenhead milkman George Kirkham was fined for telling people that there would be no newspapers that day, since London had been bombed and the presses stopped, and Charles Back of Hull got six weeks for telling people that Scarborough had been bombed. By August 1940 the Home Secretary was telling Chief Constables to deal with such cases with a caution if at all possible, unless the offence were serious or repeated. By then, he had no fewer than twenty-eight cases of such prosecutions where the case was felt to need review.

EIGHT

WAR CRIMES

Not a week passes without the Ministry of Food prosecuting hundreds of food offenders and the Board of Trade dozens of offenders against clothes rationing and quota laws. Cheating the excess profits tax is now so universally and well tried that accountants and tax inspectors no longer trouble to cross-question. . . . When food rationing was introduced it was considered smart to circumvent the law. When clothes rationing came in June 1941 it was thought to be clever to dress round the rules, convert crepe de chine sheets into dresses or blankets into coats, buy up loose coupons from street vendors, purchase clothes without coupons at dishonest shops and in general cheat the Board of Trade.

> *City journalist Nicholas Davenport, from his 1942 book*
> Vested Interests or Common Pool.

The opening months of the war saw a marked reduction in the nation's prison population. This was not, however, the result of a patriotic outbreak of law-abiding citizenship. All prisoners with less than three months to serve were released early, to make way for the influx of aliens interned in the interests of national security. (One exception to the amnesty was IRA prisoners – they got no remission, but the government did at least pay them the backhanded compliment of allowing the operation of their Special Operations Executive to be influenced by the Republican terrorist model.) The disruption of war, not to mention the blackout, created ideal conditions for crime, and the wealth of wartime regulation added a whole new repertoire of criminal offences.

A host of different factors need to be understood to unravel the crime statistics for the war years. Reported crimes rose from their 1939 level of 303,711 (England and Wales) to 478,394 in 1945, and the number of people convicted was similarly up, by 54 per cent. There was a decline in non-serious crime, which can be explained in large part by, first, the decline in motoring offences (owing to the decline in the amount of motoring) and, second, a reduction in the recorded incidence of drunkenness. This latter was due to: (a) many of the potential drunks having been recruited into the armed forces; (b) spirits being in very short supply; and (c) beer, while unrationed, being very weak and the pubs prone to running out of it. The police also showed a markedly greater tolerance towards drunkenness in wartime, as the Police Review openly admitted.

Against this, there were new classes of offence for people to commit in a heavily regulated wartime society, and the opportunity to commit them was enhanced by the cover of the blackout and the substantial reduction in the numbers of police. (Police numbers in England and Wales, including special constables, fell from 82,232 to 59,574 over the war years.) Moreover, the average age of the force rose sharply, as younger policemen joined the armed forces, and the level of sick leave also doubled.

LOOTING

Looting was one crime which attracted a particularly robust response from the authorities, as this memorandum from the Home Secretary to the Prime Minister in December 1940 shows:

> There have been many cases of looting which, though not of the gravest kind, must be regarded seriously. Damage to premises, including the shattering of windows, has led to the exposure of a great deal of valuable property, and the police are finding much difficulty in providing adequate means of protection, particularly during the hours of black-out. The temptation to take exposed goods is very great and unless drastic penalties are imposed there is substantial danger that the practice may become still more widespread. Representations have been made to me from various quarters as to the need for doing everything possible to protect those who have been injured by enemy action from suffering still further injury owing to the looting of their possessions. . . . I am told that the imposition of long sentences in certain cases has already had some deterrent effect, but looting is still a serious problem.

Churchill was concerned about both the inconsistency in sentencing policy and the severity with which some cases of looting were treated, at a time when able-bodied men were in desperately short supply. When six Auxiliary Fire Service officers received five years for stealing whisky for their own immediate consumption, he wrote to the Home Secretary:

> There seems to be great disparity in these sentences. I wonder whether any attempt is being made to standardise the punishments inflicted for this very odious crime. Five years' penal servitude for stealing whisky for immediate consumption seems out of proportion when compared to sentences of three to six months for stealing valuables. Exemplary discipline is no doubt necessary, as people must be made to feel that looting is stealing. Still, I should be glad to know that such cases are being reviewed and levelled out.

Morrison resisted pressure from the Prime Minister to promote a more lenient sentencing policy for looters, not least on the grounds that

A LIFETIME'S SUPPLY

Looting was widespread in the Channel Islands, as residents fled from the occupying forces. In one case, the Germans found the tiny flat of one James Rutter packed from floor to ceiling with more household goods and furnishings than he could have used in a lifetime. So bad was the case that even the Germans put him on trial.

sentencing policy was not part of his purview. In fact, looting had a possible maximum penalty of life imprisonment or even the death sentence, and in October 1940, the lower courts had their sentencing discretion extended from three months to a year, for those cases which came before them.

Cases of looting started to come before the courts in significant numbers more or less as soon as the bombs started to fall. September 1940 saw 539 cases come before the London courts alone, and the following month the number rose to 1,662. In February 1941 a gas company inspector reported over three thousand cases of theft from coin-operated gas meters, most of them in bombed-out houses. Intensive police efforts to combat looting in bombed areas backfired on them when burglars turned instead to the areas that had escaped bombing, which they now found to be delightfully free of police.

Press reports gave a misleading impression of the composition of the looters – 42 per cent of the guilty parties in reported cases were people in positions of trust, such as ARP wardens or fire service officials, and about 90 per cent of the reported cases had no previous criminal record. However, a fuller analysis of the cases within the metropolitan area showed that 14 per cent of the offenders were schoolboys and a full 41 per cent were under 21. Cases involving youths tended to be reported much more rarely. Some of the looting was thought to be organised – among the most macabre examples were those who entered the bombed ruins of the Café de Paris and stripped the dead of their jewellery and wallets before even the civil defence workers got in there. But the majority was spontaneous and minor. American reporter Ed Murrow found it difficult to treat some of it as a crime:

> Most of the articles picked up from the bombed houses are of little intrinsic value: a book, or a piece of ribbon, or a bucketful of coal – that sort of thing. Many people convicted of looting are certainly not criminal types and have not taken the objects for reasons of personal gain. One has a strange feeling – or at least I have – in looking at the contents of a bombed house or shop, that the things scattered about don't belong to anyone.

At first, magistrates were quite lenient in their sentencing – albeit while making much play of the possibility of the death sentence. After receiving a good deal of criticism for such leniency, the courts became much more severe, especially to those in positions of trust, whose cases tended to be referred to the Assizes for heavier sentences.

THEFT

All else being equal, one might have expected the incidence of theft to fall during the war years, since a sizeable proportion of the criminal classes would have been drafted into the armed forces. However, all that happened was that theft decreased in the inner cities and increased greatly in the areas around army camps. The arrival of the British Expeditionary Force in France was also accompanied by a small crime wave, as a significant proportion of the Army's supplies and equipment disappeared into the arms of the French black market. Special police forces had to be sent to stamp it out.

Others of a criminal bent were able to avoid the draft by taking on essential war work, such as firewatcher, where the war offered new career opportunities, such as looting. Criminals with physical handicaps, such as weak hearts or lameness, would of course be exempted from the draft. They could thereafter supplement their criminal income to the tune of up to £150 a time by impersonating others wishing to be exempted at their medical boards.

At home, wartime shortages provided a great temptation to would-be thieves, and the war saw some substantial growth in the levels of theft. The railways lost goods carried on them to the tune of £1 million in 1941 alone. Many of the railway police had joined the armed forces, and their replacements, often called out of retirement, were not always energetic enough to cope with criminals. Similarly, on the docks, pilfering had long been seen as one of the perks of a poorly paid and insecure job, as well as part of a class war against the employers. Groups of dockers operated their own form of insurance, organising a collection for any of their number who was caught and fined.

Police action against dockyard theft was also relatively selective. Anti-theft campaigns would be discontinued when the dockers' cooperation was needed (for example, during wage negotiations) and stepped up again once a deal was struck. Even so, prosecutions for theft at Birkenhead docks, for example, increased threefold between 1939 and 1942.

Ration books were a new and lucrative item to steal, with a street value of up to £5 a book. A single raid in Romford netted ration books worth £500,000, which at today's values makes the Great Train Robbery look like petty pilfering.

THE POLICE ARE IN THE DARK

The blackout provided a cover for a variety of nefarious activity, as the chapter on wartime sexual activity illustrated. In the first weeks of the war, *The Times* reported an outbreak of blackout hooliganism, with assaults on police officers under the cover of darkness being a particular problem. As Detective Sergeant Hare told Mitcham Police Court: 'Gangs of roughs are taking advantage of the blackout. It is not safe for respectable people to be about.'

The courts warned of severe punishment for such behaviour and, as an example, sentenced Mary Maher (35) of Tipperary to six months' hard labour for taking on two police officers, who were trying to advise her flatmate about the blackout regulations. This case also brought to light the unexpected potential of the gas-mask as an offensive weapon.

Petrol became a particularly prized commodity, but not everyone was equally adept at stealing it. One group of London ambulance drivers found themselves in court, after one of their number's cars ran out of petrol. They broke into the ambulance depot at night and stole a gallon from one of the vehicles. However, while trying to steal a second gallon, one of them knocked over a hurricane lamp. The ensuing blaze destroyed the garage and fifteen ambulances.

Another man, charged with the theft of 500 gallons of petrol, offered what must have been the least plausible defence in the history of crime. He told the court that he had just switched on the tap on the tank to get a few drops of petrol for his lighter, but it had gushed out and he had been forced to direct it into a large container that had just happened to be standing next to him. The magistrates gave him twelve months' hard labour, commenting: 'This offence almost amounts to treason. In any other country, the defendent would have had his head cut off for this offence.'

However, petrol thieves did at least find a use for their redundant gas-masks. Black Market petrol, stolen from commercial or military sources, contained a tell-tale red dye. By first pouring the petrol through a gas-mask, the dye could be removed and the petrol would look just like the kind bought legitimately at the petrol station (if one had the coupons, that is).

PROFITEERS

Profiteers tended to be lumped together with looters in the public consciousness: 'They do not steal and they would call themselves traders or businessmen, but they are looters none the less.' There are no separate figures for profiteering – their cases form part of the 17,319 prosecutions under the Food Control Orders undertaken between September 1939 and the end of April 1941. By September 1941 over two thousand cases per month were coming before the courts.

It had become front page news in May 1941, when a strongly worded statement by the Food Price Committee, North Midland Region, claimed that 'speculation is rampant . . . people who render no service in distribution are enriching themselves at the expense of the consumer . . . prices have in consequence risen out of all reasonable proportion . . . and the trivial fines imposed by some benches are a matter of ridicule'.

However, a contrary view was that the regulations relating to price increases were a bureaucratic nightmare that made it almost impossible for even the most honest shopkeeper to stay within the law, and that some of the prosecutions showed a bureaucratic small-mindedness that bordered on the vindictive.

In January 1940 the provisions of the 1939 Prices of Goods Act came into force. This took 21 August 1939 as the base date at which, it was assumed, prices had not been inflated by the expectation of war. The Act made it a criminal offence to sell 'price regulated' goods at more than their price at that date, plus an increase representing the actual rise in costs and expenses since that time. All over the country price regulation committees were set up to investigate complaints from the public. The first prosecution was of a shopkeeper from Reading, who had an unblemished trading record going back forty-five years. In a long and complicated case, involving the services of a chartered accountant and a near-philosophical debate about the relative qualities of imported batteries and their British counterparts, it was established that the retailer had sold two torch batteries for 10½d each more than the price permitted by the Act. The case was dismissed as a first offence, on payment of £4 13s costs.

A review of the first three months' activity by the Southern Region Price Regulation Committee hardly suggested that it was single-handedly turning the tide of the war. In that time, they carried out just three prosecutions (including the one mentioned above). Even the press could not work up enough wartime patriotism to take them entirely seriously:

Not Price Regulated. Woman's Divorce Costs.
Strange Complaints to Anti-Profiteering Committee.

A woman has written to the Price Regulation Committee for the Southern Region, complaining that she is dissatisfied with the charges made by her solicitors when she divorced her husband!

A man complained that he had paid too much for his house and wanted to know if he could be assisted to get the excess money back again!

> WATCH OUT, THERE'S A SNOOPER ABOUT
> Whole armies of snoopers were said to be on the prowl, ready if necessary to entrap the unwary shopkeeper into breaching the regulations. One popular story (said to be apocryphal) was that of the inspector disguised as a rain-soaked hiker, staggering off the moors into the village shop. He would then beg for dry socks without the necessary coupons, promising faithfully to mail them back to the shop.

These instances were related by Mr Leo Page, the Chairman of the Committee, in a press interview this week.

The Prices of Goods Act has now been in operation for three months. During that time, the Southern Region Committee has received about a hundred complaints, and at least three-quarters of them referred to articles which are not covered by the Board of Trade order. Articles included workmen's tea cans, whisky and throat pastilles.

None the less, during the course of the war, the rules were enforced with what sometimes seemed Draconian severity. One grocer was fined 7 guineas with 7 guineas costs for making 3½d excess profit over a four-month period. In no case did an individual case of his profiteering come to more than 1s 4d. Another retailer, who sold razor blades at above the approved price, was fined the amazing sum of £376 15s (including costs). His total profit on a packet of razor blades was 1s ½d.

On occasion, even the committees rebelled at the regulations they were being asked to enforce. In Birmingham the local Chairman, Mr A.L. Bill, condemned some of the cases being brought before them as 'ridiculous and trivial'. He went on: 'I hope the Committee will be more wise in future than to waste the time of the court with such trivialities.'

The cases before them on this occasion related to an overcharge of 3d on bacon and several of ¼d (i.e. a farthing) each on sugar and butter. The defendant said that the bacon overcharge was a simple oversight and that the others were simply due to a shortage of farthings. In another case a retailer confessed his ignorance of the fact that he required a licence to sell a can of peas. All but one of the cases was dismissed.

THE BLACK MARKET AND HOARDING

This is not a mere matter of self-interest. It will lighten the burden on transport in the event of war.

The *Evening Standard* before the war, encouraging housewives to lay in stocks of food.

Looking back in his memoirs, Lord Woolton, the Minister for Food, took a rather rosy view of the black market during the war: 'The penalties for the infringement of the food regulations were literally ruinous . . . and the consequence was that [black marketeering] became so perilous an occupation that few indeed dared embark on it. . . .' He also concluded, rather inconsistently, that: 'The fact that, in spite of all the scarcity of supplies and the rigidity of rationing, there was little or no black market in Britain was a tribute to the British people.'

His Ministry none the less managed to find enough evidence of it to occupy the time of 900 inspectors, armed with weapons like two years' imprisonment, £500 fines and forfeiture of capital up to three times the size of the offence.

The Field magazine, in March 1942, did not see it Lord Woolton's way:

A year ago Lord Woolton, Minister of Food, made a speech in which he promised that the Black Market would be driven out of business. In the intervening period the Black Market has grown from a small individual 'racket' into an enormous, highly efficient and totally unscrupulous organisation. Now Parliament has discussed repressive measures. So much for speeches.

Lord Woolton, one of the very few men whose Ministry has been a success, undoubtedly did his best. The Ministry of Food undertook a vast number of prosecutions, but fines mean nothing to gentry who are making enormous profits. Furthermore, these prosecutions touched only the fringe of the market. All these men with the interesting names who have been fined, and in a few cases sentenced to a month or so in prison, are the servants. The big men in business have not been touched and the big men do not object to fines at all and are not moved by prison sentences that do not touch them personally. Make no mistake about it. There are big men at the back of the Black Market; there is a big distributive organisation; there is a big warehousing organisation; there is a highly effective intelligence service. The Black Market is not made up of a large number of individuals acting independently, but a large number of individuals well organised. The thefts are on too large a scale for it to be otherwise. You cannot store 40,000 eggs nor 5 tons of meat on the kitchen shelves. And these quantities are not easy to distribute.

The Commissioner of the Metropolitan Police kept his options open in his 1944 annual report, saying that he was not able 'to substantiate by any reliable evidence the somewhat lurid descriptions published in some newspapers of super-criminals controlling a vast organisation with widespread tentacles. This may nevertheless be a true picture . . . it is significant that cases of receiving in 1944 were three and a half times as many as in 1938. . . .'

Some towns – Romford, Chelmsford, Watford and others – became particularly well known as centres of the black market. Other forms of crime – pickpocketing, gambling and illegal drinking – grew up on the back of it. Stallholders in Romford were warned by the council of instant expulsion from their pitches if they were caught in illegal dealing.

The black market grew in importance as the war went on, particularly after a military foothold was re-established in France. A popular arrangement was to take £sterling to France, where they could be sold on the black market for about 500ff each, two and a half times their official rate. This was then used to buy liqueurs, perfumes, silk stockings, cosmetics and other items unobtainable in Britain. So great was the volume of material flowing into the country (there were even reports of planes being chartered for the purpose) that black market prices were themselves depressed in a flooded market.

Another favourite trick was for a trader to buy up the short end of a lease on a shop, fill the window with a lot of flashy, cheap goods and, once potential customers were lured in, offer them all sorts of black market commodities at inflated prices. He would make his profit and be gone before the authorities caught up with him. Other traders would impose a rule that customers could not buy the item they wanted unless they also bought another, unwanted, item with it.

The officials trying to enforce trading rules were swamped with the volume of the work and boggled by the complexity of the wartime legislation. This offered a wealth of loopholes to the unscrupulous trader. Eggs sold for breeding purposes were exempted from rationing. Defective and most second-hand goods were also exempt. Health regulations were also flouted in the food shortage – horsemeat was sold as beef and diseased and otherwise unfit meat found its way on to the market.

Rationing opened up vast opportunities for fraud and theft at every stage of the process. The coupons were much easier to forge than the banknotes which had been a flourishing pre-war industry; crooked postmen would steal ration books when delivering them, in addition to the other thefts mentioned earlier. Coupons were only supposed to be removed by the shopkeeper, except when goods were being bought by mail order. This loophole opened up a massive market in the sale of coupons, especially by the poor, who did not have the cash to benefit from the ration themselves.

Various frauds were available to obtain extra coupons. In the first year of clothes rationing, around 800,000 people lost their ration books, and 27 million new coupons were issued as replacements. No doubt many of these losses were genuine, but a proportion were not. Some people adopted dual identities, and claimed the ration books to go with them. Anyone presenting themselves as being bombed out could qualify for 120 clothing coupons and £12 from the Assistance Board.

Retailers used to exchange the coupons they collected at the post office for vouchers, with which they could buy more rationed goods for sale. The GPO refused to take on the fiddly job of counting envelopes full of individual coupons, and it was left to random (and not sufficiently frequent) checks by Ministry officials. As a result, some of the envelopes handed in contained far fewer than the number of coupons claimed, or even just pieces of paper torn from the telephone directory. Finally, even used coupons, on their way to be pulped, were sometimes stolen and 'recycled'.

New classes of criminal were created by wartime rationing. Deserters from the army, of whom there were an estimated twenty thousand by the end of the war, had no ration books and no papers, and were virtually forced to turn to crime. Normally law-abiding citizens were driven to evade the ration by a scheme which, from 1942, only gave a man a new overcoat every seven years, a new pullover every five years and a new shirt every twenty months.

HOARDING

Hoarding of goods also became a serious offence during the war, though in the immediate pre-war period retailers encouraged their customers to buy in a good stock of non-perishable foods in against future shortages. The new post of Food Executive Officer was created, whose job it was to track down hoarders like this case, reported in the *Berkshire Chronicle* in 1942:

> ### Food Hoarding Prosecution. Caversham Woman Fined.
> ### Defence Plea that she acted Innocently.
>
> Mrs Elsie Lilian Carter, of 10a Bridge Street, Caversham, appeared at Reading Borough Police Court on Monday on five summonses of food hoarding. It was alleged that the defendant had acquired an excessive quantity of preserves and of tinned fruit, tinned steak, fish and milk.
>
> It was stated for the prosecution that these were the first proceedings to be taken by the Reading Borough Food Executive Officer for food hoarding. An excess quantity of food referred to anything in excess of the household's requirements for seven days. In this case, the household comprised two persons. An Inspector was sent to this address in consequence of information received. He asked Mrs Carter to show him her stores, and she opened the door of a kitchen cupboard in which there was a fairly generous supply of household commodities, such as one would expect to find in any normal household. The Inspector asked Mrs Carter if she had any other stores, to save him searching the house. She replied, 'If I have, it has slipped my memory.'
>
> In a recess under the stairs and in an adjoining cupboard the Inspector afterwards found large quantities of food. These included 75lb of preserves, 196 tins of fish, 82 tins of milk, 81 tins of meat and 98 tins of mixed fruit. Invoices were produced in court to show that the stores were purchased wholesale from Messrs Kingham since the beginning of the war.
>
> On behalf of his client, Mr Berry submitted that none of the goods had been purchased during a period when they had been rationed, so there could be no

breach of the rationing orders. . . . Mrs Carter had acted innocently under a misapprehension that she was doing the right thing, a misapprehension due to taking notice of government pamphlets.

In announcing fines on the five summonses totalling £36 15s, the Chairman, Mr A.G. West, said that the bench considered it a bad case of hoarding. In addition to the fines, the defendant would have to pay £10 10s costs.

Mrs Carter was allowed one month to pay. Mr Edminson said that the Ministry of Food had the power, if they chose to exercise it, to requisition the food stocks upon payment of the wholesale prices. I do not know if that procedure would be followed in the case of Mrs Carter.

OFFICERS AND GENTLEMEN

At a time when one's rank could be the key to success, from social advancement to winning the hearts of the opposite sex, the courts saw a regular stream of cases of people impersonating officers. So it was that James Fisher, of no fixed abode, found himself up before the court for impersonating a captain in the Royal Horse Guards, complete with DSO, MC and the French Croix de Guerre (all that was missing from his set, it seems, was the Iron Cross).

He told the court that it was just vanity and over-keenness on his part. He had served in the First World War, retiring as a captain, and had applied to serve again. The result of his application was pending, but it cannot have been helped when, on learning that he had a previous conviction for a similar offence, the court put him away for three months.

In similar vein, a 27-year-old dockyard labourer from Gillingham, Alfred Hancock, got two months' hard labour for impersonating an RAF flight lieutenant. He pointed out to the court how easy it was to do. Most of the leading tailors offered a service of making officers' uniforms to measure and there appeared to be little or no control over who ordered them. The Chairman of the Magistrates observed 'it seems to us most unfortunate'.

For those who wished to take their delusion to a higher level, there was always the prospect of trying to buy yourself a proper commission. Sir Curtis George Lampson (Bart) got eighteen months for inciting a young man to offer an inducement to obtain a commission in the army. The victim was told that, for £600, a commission could be obtained within twenty-four hours. Lampson promised to see a viscount of his acquaintance, to arrange it. The viscount was, of course, non-existent. As the War Office pointed out: 'It cannot be said too strongly that there is nobody in the War Office who could be approached in this way. This sort of thing does not and cannot happen.'

Others found a far cheaper alternative than buying uniforms or commissions. Alfred Jones of Wednesfield had always fancied being a policeman, and decided, while drunk, that the time had come to get some practice in. He staggered up to a member of the public and, claiming to be a plain-clothes policeman, asked him to accompany him to the station. The person approached did not believe him, but summoned a real police officer who promptly did just what Jones had asked. He was fined £1. Another 17-year-old youth told a young lady of his acquaintance that he was a secret service agent. He gave her a 'secret' letter to take care of and later phoned her, pretending to be an air commodore. He told her that the 'secret agent' had been killed parachuting into enemy territory and asked her to bring the secret letter to a special rendezvous. The young lady sent it via a policeman and the would-be James Bond found himself in court.

JUVENILE CRIME AND CORPORAL PUNISHMENT

A considerable increase in juvenile crime is causing concern in many districts; the explanation given is generally the slackening of parental control, coupled with the unsettling effect of unprecedented high wages, which are now being paid to boys who take the place of men. . . . It is thought by social workers that lack of any incentive to save, plus the fact that there are few reasonable pleasures on which to spend this 'easy money', must create serious danger for young people, at a time when violence and destruction on a vast scale are inevitably held up as an admirable human activity.

A Liverpool schoolmaster alleges that in the city there are at least 200 'cellar clubs' where boys and girls indulge in 'an orgy of gambling and drinking'.

There has been some increase in the volume of complaints . . . particularly of the immorality of young girls and the behaviour of children. There is particular concern about the damaging of property: breaking of windows, slashing of cinema seats, smashing electric light bulbs in trains, and damage to parks and gardens are alleged.

Factors blamed are:

(a) Lack of parental control, particularly where mothers are at work. Women, it is suggested, should not be able to take up full-time jobs unless they are able to satisfy the authorities that their children will be looked after in their absence.

(b) The irresponsibility of parents, particularly of working mothers 'with money to spare', who spend their time in pubs and cinemas.

These two Home Intelligence reports, from July 1941 and June 1944 respectively, highlight the growing problem of youth crime during the war years. The causes identified by the complainants are in some cases unique to the war, but in many others are common to the years of peace and prosperity that were to follow. The delinquent behaviour described in the second extract could have come just as easily from a report on 1950s teddy boys or the mods and rockers of the 1960s.

A Home Office circular published in the middle of 1941 reported that in the first year of the war there had been a 41 per cent increase in the

> ### FRAUD AMONG THE DOLLY MIXTURES
> 'We had a shop down our road; a blind lady was the proprietor. We used to put a piece of blotting paper under the sweet coupon page on the ration book, and trace round it and cut out the blotting paper in the shape of coupons. The old lady felt the texture and shape of the blotting paper and was deceived into thinking it was the coupons and we took the sweets.'
>
> Girl aged six, quoted in Westall.

numbers of under-14s found guilty of indictable offences. The increase in the 14–17 age group was 22 per cent. Among other causes, the government blamed unsettled wartime domestic circumstances, with many more absent fathers and mothers working, leading to increased truancy. But in some areas of major cities it was impossible at times not to be truant, since all the schools had been closed in anticipation of a total evacuation of schoolchildren. Thus eighty thousand schoolchildren were running wild in London by the end of 1940.

Amateur sociologists were not short of other explanations for the growth of juvenile crime, which had started before the war – when they had blamed unemployment and boredom. Now, for some perverse reason, it was said to be due to the high salaries payable to young people in war work. Then there was the growth of the get-rich-quick society, also marked by the import of American fashions. The Chief Constable of Nottingham, Captain Popkess, drew a comparison in his 1937 annual report between the growth in juvenile crime in Britain and its almost complete absence in Germany. This, he explained, was mainly due to the wholesome influence of the Hitler Youth movement. A more plausible explanation for a pre-war growth in recorded juvenile crime was a change in the way young people were dealt with, following the 1933 Children and Young Persons Act.

During the early years of the war, the figures cannot have been helped by the fact that all Borstal inmates who had served over six months of their sentence were freed as part of the general clearout of the prison population. Left with no support, about half of these young people had re-offended by the end of the war.

Some magistrates responded to the rising tide of crime by having a growing number of young offenders birched. But a case in Hereford drew attention to the incompatibility between birching and the right of appeal. On 12 January 1943 two boys aged 11 and 13 were found guilty of malicious damage, following break-ins at a school and a hostel. They were placed in care and sentenced to 4 strokes of the birch each. The sentence was carried out before they had a chance to have their appeal heard, making it somewhat superfluous. There was a considerable public outcry about this case, and the Home Secretary was forced to intervene, telling Parliament that corporal punishment was not considered a suitable remedy for young offenders.

Public opinion was found to be divided on the matter of birching young offenders. The majority sided with the Home Secretary, but a sizeable minority supported the Chief Constable of Renfrewshire, who said with blood-curdling relish that he would 'use a green birch and cut them with it'. A Home Office memorandum at the end of the war cast doubt on the efficacy of birching as a deterrent and showed that its use had declined steadily since 1941, well before the publicity given to the issue by the Hereford case.

NINE

WOMEN AT WAR

What changes did the war bring about in the position of women? Both wars were said to have wrought, or at least accelerated, changes, opening up new areas of career opportunity and changing their legal status. In the First World War the Representation of the People Act 1918 gave the vote to married women over 30, though it took another ten years' campaigning for women to be given the vote on an equal footing with men. There was some debate as to whether it would have happened anyway – whether the climate of opinion had been prepared for an extension of the franchise before war broke out – but it was at least presented in some government circles as a recognition of their contribution to the war effort. Was there any comparable change in the situation of women during the Second World War?

At the time the coalition government formed, in May 1940, there were only twelve women MPs in Parliament. They used to meet in a lady members' room, known as 'the boudoir', to work out common policies across party lines. Even so, there were divisions among them, between those who wanted equality and those who wanted measures to take the pressure off working-class women – what might be characterised as the 'free milk' movement. They none the less had some successes, such as promoting a cross-party Woman Power Committee.

Before the war, women in the civil service (and in some other professions) were expected to resign upon getting married. Many chose instead to live in sin, or to keep their marriage a secret, rather than lose their jobs. Some 300,000 married women were thought to be doing this at the outbreak of war. Over and above this, there were moves from among the male staff to ban all women entirely from working in the service. An anti-feminist organisation called Fairfield was set up in 1939, with this as one of its central aims. It attracted three thousand members in the first four months of its existence.

EQUAL PAY

Three main attempts were made to secure recognition at least of the principle of equal pay for women during the war years. In December 1941 a group of MPs attempted to block the National Service (Number Two) Act, which sought to conscript certain groups of women, unless a provision for equal pay was included. They failed in this, not least because the Act discriminated in favour of women in other ways – for example, no mother of a child aged under 14 could be conscripted, and only single women between 19 and 30 were covered by the legislation. By 1943 women up to the age of 50 could be directed into war work, but even then, a woman's duties as a housewife were sufficient to exempt her from full-time service.

The 1939 Personal Injuries Act was a long-standing target of women's interest groups. Under this, a woman suffering injuries from a bomb received 7s per week less than a man receiving comparable injuries. There was widespread public support for equality of treatment in these circumstances – Hitler's bombs, at least, did not exercise any discrimination about whom they landed on.

But even here, the case was argued (at least in part) in a way which was discriminatory towards women, treating them as chattels. One of the arguments commonly advanced against equal pay for women at the time was that they would normally be able to rely upon their husband's income, and therefore did not have the same need of independent means. However, in this case, a woman injured by a bomb was deemed to have worse prospects for marriage, and it was therefore held to be wrong in these circumstances to treat them as dependants for compensation purposes.

The government finally conceded the principle of equal compensation in this case in April 1943. One of the reasons why it was able to do so was that the circumstances related so clearly to war conditions that they offered up no precedent for the post-war world.

The third battle for equal pay came in the context of the 1944 Education Act's passage through Parliament. Here, the House narrowly voted in favour of including a provision for equal pay for teachers. The government, strongly urged by Winston Churchill, reintroduced the matter back into the House and turned it into a vote of confidence. The War Cabinet argued that: 'It would be disastrous to depart from the principle of non-interference with the decisions of independent tribunals on wage questions.'

In short, they feared that the precedent would have disastrous knock-on effects throughout the economy. The proposal was defeated and the government kicked the whole business into the long grass for the duration of the war by setting up a Royal Commission on Equal Pay. This did not report until 1946, and its damp squib of a report reinforced many of the traditional prejudices against women in the workplace – that they were less efficient than men, primarily home-focused and generally not the main breadwinner.

FAMILY ALLOWANCE – MOTHER'S BONUS

Family Allowance was one of the few parts of the Welfare State introduced during the war years. But one aspect of it which impinged upon women was the question of to whom it belonged. Eleanor Rathbone MP campaigned for twenty-five years for the payment of Family Allowance as a recognition of the value of a mother's work.

The government's Reconstruction Committee decided that either parent should be able to collect the benefit, but that it had to 'belong' to one parent or the other for legal purposes. They chose the father, as the person legally responsible for the child's maintenance, and because Family Allowance was designed to supplement family income, not to provide in full for the needs of the child. The government did not want to do anything to weaken the father's sense of responsibility for the upkeep of his children. They were heavily lobbied against this, and threatened with a coalition-breaking amendment in Parliament. It was finally decided to put the matter to a free vote, which went in favour of the mothers.

Meanwhile, male opposition to equal pay even found its way into sabotage. Night-shift workers in a factory in Birmingham deliberately loosened the bolts on a lathe to slow down its female day-shift user, regardless of the fact that it could have caused a serious accident. One of the few recommendations the Commission did make was to introduce equal pay for equal work in the 'common classes' of the civil service, where men and women worked together. But given that the civil service operated its own version of sexual apartheid, even this modest proposal was less than met the eye. None the less the Labour government of the day rejected even that, on the grounds that the nation could not afford it.

WHAT'S THINE IS MINE, DEAR

Even a married woman's savings were not her own. In a controversial and widely reported case in October 1943, the Court of Appeal found against Mrs Dorothy Blackwell, ruling that her £103 10s savings were not hers, but those of her husband, from whom she had been separated since 1941. She had saved them from her housekeeping allowance and from taking in lodgers from 1936 onwards. In summing up, the judges came down strongly in favour of the wife as chattel:

Lord Justice Goddard suggested that she might let her husband go short of food while she 'built up a bank account'. Facetiously, he pictured her giving him corned beef instead of roast beef for dinner. It would, he said, be 'a dreadful thing' to hold that her savings were her own; it would tempt husbands to stint their wives. . . . Lord Justice Goddard opined that even if a married couple agreed that the savings out of the housekeeping money should be the wife's, such agreement would not necessarily constitute a legal contract. . . .

Dismissing the appeal, Lord Justice Scott said: 'There is no justification at all for the contention that where a husband hands to his wife an allowance for housekeeping purposes, the husband is not to be taken, as a matter of law, as presenting savings out of that money to the wife for her sole use.' Meanwhile, Dr (Edith) Summerskill, supported by 43 other MPs, has tabled a motion calling for the amendment of the Married Women's Property Act 1882, to secure to married women a legal right to reasonable savings from their housekeeping allowance.

The Catholic Citizen, 15 November 1943.

Home Intelligence found much public criticism of what was seen to be an antiquated law, though some husbands apparently found some amusement in it. They argued that wise housewives would not support the paying of a wage by a husband, as this 'would jeopardise the comradeship of married life'. Joking aside, the idea of companionate marriage had spread into the country from America in the inter-war years, and it is sometimes argued that the rising expectations of marriage arising from this were a contributory factor to the rising divorce rate after the war, discussed elsewhere.

A WOMAN'S PLACE . . . IS IN THE FACTORY

Before the war there was, in many parts of society, a strong tradition that a woman's place was in the home. During the First World War there had been industrial unrest when the government had tried to introduce women into traditionally male workplaces. Safeguards, such as legislation to guarantee that everything went back to pre-war practices once hostilities finished, had to be introduced. Ernest Bevin, the wartime Minister of Labour, was the pre-war head of the Transport and General Workers' Union. He knew that if women were to replace the missing male workers, it needed to be done as far as possible with the consent of the management and unions. He therefore set up joint consultative committees to negotiate the process. By giving trades unions equal representation with management on them (a marked improvement from the trades unions' distinctly second-class status in the days of Neville Chamberlain) he eased the way for an extra 1.5 million women to move into essential industries between 1939 and 1943.

It was no easy task to achieve the shift in the workforce. Fewer than half the women made redundant from non-essential industries during the first year of Churchill's premiership found their way into war industries. This was in no small part due to the boring and unpleasant nature of much of the work. Advertising campaigns were run during 1941, including the War Work Week parades and such memorable slogans as 'Don't queue like shirkers, join the women workers'.

This slogan, portraying the hard-pressed wartime housewife as 'a shirker', occasioned some resentment from both housewives and their husbands. Women pointed out that if they went out to work, there would be war at home, and one air raid warden spoke for many husbands:

> If married women are called up home life will vanish and it will be very hard to revive it after the war. . . . Men in reserved occupations will come back to cold, untidy houses with no meal ready. Friction in the home will be greatly increased and with children evacuated there will be nothing to hold it together.

Eventually, conscription became one of the main means by which Bevin expanded the workforce. He was also helped by the economic necessity forced upon many wives whose husbands had been called up.

One of the ways in which he achieved this was by 'dilution' – the automation and de-skilling of traditional craft jobs. The unions were distinctly uneasy about this, and one of the prices Bevin paid for it was the 1942 Restoration of Pre-War Practices Act, a parallel to the First World War legislation ensuring a restoration of the status quo (and a reversal of any advances women had made) at the end of hostilities.

The unions also supported equal pay for women workers doing men's work – they did not want employers to be offered any financial incentive to replace their male members on a long-term basis. This was conceded, but with a number of qualifications. First, women moved only gradually up to the full male rate for the job; secondly, they only got it if they required no additional supervision or support to do the job; thirdly, employers were able to deny women male rates for jobs commonly performed by women, even if the individual concerned actually replaced a male worker. The management spent a good deal of time trying to prove that this or that task was commonly performed by women in pre-war years, and the unions were unhappy at this 'feminisation' of their members' work.

Management generally devoted much ingenuity to getting round the demands for equal pay. Lack of skills was one of the reasons most frequently cited for women's failure to advance, yet they constituted only 5 per cent of those on Government skills training schemes (and most of these were studying typing or sewing). When male and female workers – equally untrained – were brought in to operate machines in Rolls-Royce's

Hillington factory near Glasgow in 1943, the men were put on to a higher grade. This led in October to a strike by the women workers, supported by most of the men. The dispute was finally resolved by attaching a grading system to each machine. But the grading system was itself gender-related. In practice, very few of the additional women drafted in to the essential industries moved into the most skilled and highly paid grades.

The government itself had no intention of interfering with the time-honoured practice of sex discrimination in the workplace, as this Treasury evidence to a Parliamentary Committee made clear:

> The principle of sex discrimination, whether it is right or wrong, is at present a matter of government policy, and it runs right through a large part of the social structure . . . the government should provide payment and observe conditions which corresponded to the best practice in comparable outside occupations, but it was not contemplated that the Government should run ahead of outside practice, and of course, sex differentiation is deeply embedded in industrial and – though to a slightly lesser extent – in commercial practice. . . .

HOME AND WORK

Childcare was another of the factors that gave women the ability to work, and considerable numbers of places were eventually provided at day nurseries for the children of working mothers. However, the initiative got off to a slow start: by the start of 1941 only fourteen government-sponsored nurseries had been set up. The best efforts of the Ministry of Labour were often achieved over the dead bodies of the Ministry of Health and its local representative, the Medical Officer of Health. They tended to oppose the principle of workers' nurseries, fearing epidemics and traumatised children and mothers. Mothers who wanted (or needed) to work held their own demonstrations – 'baby riots' as the tabloid press called them. They stopped the traffic with their prams and chanted 'We want war work, we want nurseries'. Even so, there were never places for more than 25 per cent of all the children of working mothers, and many of these places rapidly disappeared with the ending of hostilities, again reversing the economic progress of women in the immediate post-war years.

The government made more or less half-hearted attempts to ease the passage of women into work. Circulars were sent to factory managers, showing them how to clean up the toilets and generally make their premises more female-friendly. Women welfare officers – known as Bevin's Belles – were sent round to advise factories on improvements and to fit women to the right jobs. The advice they offered would not always pass as enlightened today. Take, for example, this, in relation to women over 35:

'A factory like ours always has a lot of more or less 'childish' jobs that would irk a lively youngster in five minutes, but which we find ideal for the grannies.'

The traditional home-centred view of women was also emphasised by the Ministry of Information. Films such as *Jane Brown changes her job* and *Night Shift* introduced what must have been sickening paragons of virtue to many of the audience – women who could take on a full-time job without sacrificing any of their feminine qualities. They were expected to be a hostess in the sitting room, chef in the kitchen, lathe operator in the factory (and in the bedroom? For 1940s audiences, possibly an ARP officer, checking the blackout?). Women's magazines and newspapers also promoted the theme of 'beauty as duty'. For example:

Women can help Win the War.
Bright Clothes create Cheerful Atmosphere

That clothes make the man is not really true, because many of the best men wear the best clothes and it is no easier to judge the real quality of a man than a baked potato by its jacket.

That women's clothes make the man is, however, undoubtedly true. If they are the right kind of clothes, snappy and bright and smart, they will make him cheerful and bright, too; if they are stuffy and dowdy and uninteresting they will be as depressing as an empty tobacco pouch to an air raid warden on a cold and foggy night. This aspect of the question is surely more important at wartime than at any other.

Modern wars are fought psychologically as well as physically, and no psychological campaign will achieve a greater victory than the campaign for brightness and cheer. This is a campaign that women can fight as well as men, and it is fought not with guns and tanks and suchlike nasty rough things, but with lovely crepe, satin and lovely moiré, which can provide a variety of life and brilliance and colouring that will put miles on to the marching power of the British Army.

This rhetoric was translated into hard decisions on the munitions front. Supplies of scarce steel and rubber were set aside to safeguard the supply of ladies' corsets; a fashion couturier was brought in to design nether garments for the women's services. Supplies of high-grade cosmetics were made available to women munitions workers, whose occupation left them prone to discoloration of the skin; ladies' hairdressers were in some cases designated as key war workers.

For most women workers, the supply of corsets ranked fairly low on their scale of concerns. More immediate were the practical problems of trying to combine the interminable queues in the shops with the long hours of war work in the factories. As we saw elsewhere, this caused a good deal of ill-feeling against those middle-class women who were able to get away with 'voluntary' war work, which allowed them much more time off, when required. A Ministry of Labour study in 1942 highlighted the scale of the problems the working wife faced:

> A married woman with a house, a husband and children already has a full-time job which is difficult to carry out these days. Yet thousands of them are working long hours in factories. They are trying to do two full-time jobs. If they carry on with a mere half day per week off in ordinary factory hours they are achieving something marvellous.

Mass Observation also warned against the consequences of over-stretching the female labour force:

> While winning the war is the only big consideration . . . if the bonds of family and continuity are weakened beyond a certain point, the morale, unity and work effort of the country is weakened.
>
> There are thought to be still a lot of men who are avoiding fire-watching duty; women feel that all men should be called upon first. It is suggested that the ARP Service and the Home Guard, 'who spend long hours of duty doing nothing' and older men up to 65 or 70, should be brought in to fire watch.
>
> Fire watching is not a fit job for women; this opinion appears to be held chiefly by men, who are said to be doubtful of women's ability to tackle difficult fires, and dubious about the propriety of girls being on duty with men employees at night.
>
> Fire watching in target areas should be left to men; women should only fire watch in residential areas.
>
> Women's Fire Guard order, Home Intelligence report, 27 August 1942.

TEN

THE LEGACY OF WAR

... the purpose of victory is to live in a better world than the old world
... each individual is more likely to concentrate upon his war effort if
he feels that his government will be ready with plans for that better
world ... if these plans are to be ready in time, they must be made
now.

William Beveridge.

Did the war result in dramatic changes in post-war British society? During
the war years there was much talk (albeit discouraged by the Conservative
part of the wartime coalition) of the better world that Britons were fighting
for. *Picture Post* magazine published an influential special edition in January
1941 under the title *A plan for Britain*. In it, they discussed much of what
was to be the agenda for domestic politics in the war and immediately post-
war years: social security, full employment, education and health reforms,
and the need for land-use planning. Their editorial forged the link between
the nation's war aims and what came after:

> Our plan for a new Britain is not something outside the war, or something after
> the war. It is an essential part of our war aims. It is, indeed, our most positive war
> aim. The new Britain is the country we are fighting for. And the kind of land we
> want, the kind of life we think the good life, will exercise an immense attraction
> over the oppressed peoples of Europe and the friendly peoples of America. . . .
>
> We believe that, after this war, certain things will be common ground among all
> political parties. It will be common ground, for example, that every Briton – man,
> woman or child – shall be assured of enough food of the right kinds to maintain
> him in full bodily health and fitness. It will be common ground that we must
> reform our system of education – so that every child is assured of the fullest
> education he can profit by. It will be common ground that our state medical
> service must be reorganised and developed so as to foster health, not merely battle
> with disease. It will be common ground that the agricultural land of Britain must
> not again be given up to thistles and bracken; and that the beauty of our country
> and our buildings is the nation's heritage, not to be pawned away in plots to
> speculative builders.

Churchill attempted to kick the whole question of post-war reconstruction
into the long grass for the duration, by making some token gestures
towards the reformers. He set up a toothless War Aims Committee in

August 1940, and in January 1941 gave responsibility for questions of post-war reconstruction to a failing Labour politician with a drink problem, Arthur Greenwood.

One of the papers submitted to the War Aims Committee, by the historian Arnold Toynbee, effectively set out the outlines of what came to be the Welfare State. Beveridge was not working in a vacuum. Many of the ideas he and others were advancing had become accepted wisdom among progressive intellectuals before the war, and it is unlikely that something along the lines of the Welfare State would have been long delayed had the war not intervened. In some respects, what Beveridge proposed was relatively conservative: it required contributions from workers, employers and the state, had flat rates of benefit and did not even produce a bare subsistence income. Subsistence levels of payment were to be gradually phased in but, by the mid-1950s, some 27 per cent of pensioner households were still receiving means-tested National Assistance supplements to their state pensions.

The only part of the Welfare State to be implemented during the war years was the Family Allowances Act of 1945. This paid 5*s* weekly to the mother for each child after the first. Some liked to think that the Act was prompted by high-minded concern about child poverty, which was thrown into such sharp relief by the evacuation. In fact, Churchill and his chancellor were more concerned with stimulating the birth rate and with finding a cheaper alternative to universal wage increases for doing so.

The one other major piece of supposedly reforming legislation to surface during the war years was the 1944 Education Act – the so-called Butler Act. But this achieved neither of the goals reformers wanted – equality of opportunity and improved technical education. Local authorities were empowered, rather than required, to take action, and the lack of vision of the Act has been blamed for Britain's poor post-war economic performance. One of its provisions – the raising of the school leaving age to fifteen – had been due to happen in September 1939, had not events elsewhere intervened. This aside, the Act was to a large degree a preserver of the status quo – protecting public and direct grant schools, making religious education mandatory, but doing little for scientific and technical education. Perhaps the greatest achievement of the Act was that it got on to the statute book at all, given Churchill's reluctance to legislate about education. It did so partly to give the Conservatives some credibility as a reforming party, at a time when they were doing their best to obstruct or water down Beveridge's welfare state proposals.

> Colonel Blimp explains:
> 'Education must be stopped. If people couldn't read, they wouldn't know about the depression and confidence would be restored.'

The greatest single concern for the future among the wartime public was of a return to pre-war levels of mass unemployment. The 1944 White Paper on employment was supposed to address this, but in fact papered over the gulf which divided the wartime coalition partners on the matter. It was internally inconsistent and was condemned by both Labour's Aneurin Bevan and Conservative Party Chairman Ralph Assheton as a sham.

Land-use planning was another area that bitterly divided the coalition parties. Labour wanted comprehensive planning powers to help sweep away the legacy of polluted and overcrowded Victorian slums, to prevent ribbon development and to protect areas of natural beauty. The Conservatives were instinctively opposed to the state intervention involved and again did all that they could to delay and water down the proposals, short of outright opposition to what was at the time a very popular proposal. Again, a White Paper was prepared in an effort to conceal the divisions within government. It failed to do so, and was eventually shelved. The differences were never resolved. The Labour government in 1947, freed from the constraints of coalition, introduced comprehensive land-use planning, and one of the first acts of the next Conservative government in 1951 was to repeal some of its most important provisions.

Health reform was on the Labour agenda before it entered the wartime coalition. In this case, wartime demands on medical services meant that a form of *de facto* nationalisation of the private health sector was unavoidable, and, like Social Insurance, it was an idea whose time had come, regardless of the war. Wartime surveys showed that there was a majority of the population in favour of a National Health Service in all sectors of the population. Some of the main opposition to it came from within the medical profession itself. They were supported by the caretaker 1945 Conservative government, which produced an NHS White Paper which the official history of the Service describes as 'one of capitulation (to the BMA) rather than the emergence of consensus'. This was duly scrapped by the new Labour government, whose 1946 National Health Service Act was based on its own thinking.

The war years thus did little to produce new solutions to pre-war concerns with poverty, inequality, the environment and health. Neither did they produce any advances in the role of women to rival the granting of the vote after the First World War. As the previous chapter showed, trade union pressure ensured that most of the advances women made into new areas of employment were reversed, once peace was restored. Most of the workplace nursery provision disappeared, some employers reintroduced their bans on married women employees and many more applied a very restrictive policy on working practices that made their position more difficult. The post-war baby boom (birth rates rose from their lowest ever recorded level – 13.9/1000 in 1941 – to a record high of 20.6/1000 in

1947) left an increasing proportion of women with domestic responsibilities. By 1951 the proportion of women in the workforce had fallen back to its pre-war level.

Not everyone saw the advances made by women in the wartime economy as progress. One speaker in a debate in Parliament in 1945 referred to the war years for women as 'these empty wasted years, sacrificed in war; years deprived of husband, often of home and of the children we long to have'.

The Conservatives at their 1945 Party Conference considered the following resolution:

> That with the object of maintaining in the peace the partnership between men and women as full citizens that has proved so successful in war, this Conference affirms its belief that it is in the interest of the nation that opportunities and rewards shall be open equally to both sexes in order to ensure that the best mind or hand shall have the same chance to excel.

They threw it out.

But one thing had changed. If the Archbishop of Canterbury was to be believed, Britain found itself on the edge of a moral abyss. In July 1945 the Archbishop called upon his flock to reject wartime morality and return to a Christian way of life. He spoke of:

> . . . the increase in divorce, the declining birth rate, the spread of venereal disease, and the number of young couples who, as always in wartime, wed in haste without any intention of fulfilling the primary purposes of marriage. This is partly due to the influence of wartime conditions, and partly to the flaunting sale of contraceptives.

But this was one genie that would not go back into the lamp. It has been suggested that the changed moral climate that the war produced, and the increasing immunity to shock over matters sexual that came from continued exposure to black propaganda, laid the foundation for the excesses of the swinging sixties, some twenty years in the future as the first post-war generation grew to maturity.

BIBLIOGRAPHY

Addison, Paul, *The road to 1945* (Pimlico 1994)

Bousquet, Ben and Douglas, Colin, *West Indian women at war* (Lawrence & Wishart 1991)

Bryant, Mark (ed), *The complete Colonel Blimp* (Bellew 1991)

Bunting, Madeleine, *The model occupation* (HarperCollins 1995)

Calder, Angus, *The myth of the Blitz* (Cape 1991)

Chamberlin, E.R., *Life in wartime Britain* (Batsford 1972)

Cockett, Richard, *Twilight of truth* (Weidenfeld & Nicholson 1989)

Colpi, Terry, *The Italian factor* (Mainstream 1991)

Costello, John, *Love, sex and war* (Collins 1985)

De Courcy, Anne, *1939: The last season* (Thames & Hudson 1989)

Dewey, Peter, *War and progress: Britain 1914–45* (Longman 1997)

Donnelly, Mark, *Britain in the Second world war* (Routledge 1999)

Ferris, Paul, *Sex and the British* (Michael Joseph 1993)

Fitzgibbon, Constantine, *The Blitz* (Macdonald 1957)

Fussell, Paul, *Wartime* (Oxford University Press 1989)

Gillman, Peter and Leni, *Collar the Lot!* (Quartet 1980)

Glover, Michael, *Invasion scare 1940* (Leo Cooper 1990)

Grafton, Pete, *You, you and you!* (Pluto Press 1981)

Haining, Peter, *The day war broke out* (W.II. Allen 1989)

Hamilton, Neil, *Great political eccentrics* (Robson 1990)

Hinsley, F.H., *British Intelligence in the Second World War* (HMSO 1993)

Hopkins, Eric, *A social history of the English working classes* (Hodder & Stoughton 1979)

Humphries, Steve, *A secret world of sex* (Sidgwick & Jackson 1988)

Jackson, Carlton, *Who will take our children?* (Methuen 1985)

Kushner, Tony, *The persistence of prejudice* (Manchester University Press 1989)

Laybourn, Keith, *Britain on the breadline* (Sutton 1990)

Lewis, Peter, *A people's war* (Thames Methuen 1986)

Livesey, Anthony (ed), *Are we at war? Letters to the Times* (Times Books 1989)

Longmate, Norman, *The real Dads' Army, the story of the Home Guard* (Hutchinson 1974)

Lynton, Mark, *Accidental Journey* (Overlook 1995)

Macmillan, James, *The way it happened 1935–50* (William Kimber 1980)

Marwick, Arthur, *The Home Front* (Thames & Hudson 1976)

McLaine, Ian, *Ministry of morale* (George Allen & Unwin 1979)

Miller, Neil, *Out of the past* (Vintage 1995)

Nicholls, Beverley, *The unforgiving minute* (W.H. Allen 1978)

Parsons, Martin, *I'll take that one* (Beckett Karlson 1998)

Ponting, Clive, *1940: Myth and reality* (Hamish Hamilton 1990)

Purvis, June (ed), *Women's history: Britain 1850–1945* (UCL Press 1995)

Readers' Digest, *Life on the Home Front* (Readers' Digest 1993)

Rowbotham, Sheila, *A century of women* (Viking 1997)

Schactman, Tom, *The Phoney War 1939–40* (Harper & Row 1982)

Smith, Harold L (ed), *Britain in the Second World war, A social history* (Manchester University Press 1996)

Smithies, Edward, *Crime in wartime* (George Allen & Unwin 1982)

Spectator, *Articles of War: the Spectator book of World War Two* (Grafton 1989)

Stent, Ronald, *A bespattered page? The internment of 'HM most loyal aliens'* (Deutsch 1980)

Taylor, Eric, *Women who went to war* (Robert Hale 1988)

Valery, Anne, *Talking about the war* (Michael Joseph 1991)

Weale, Adrian, *Renegades: Hitler's Englishmen* (Weidenfeld & Nicholson 1994)

Westall, Robert, *Children of the Blitz* (Viking 1985)

Wicks, Ben, *No time to say goodbye* (Bloomsbury 1988)

Ziegler, Philip, *London at war* (Sinclair Stevenson 1995)

INDEX

A few pathetic remains, rescued from a bombed-out house in 'a south-east inland town' in February 1943. On the extreme left, a policeman stands guard over them and a notice in the window warns of life imprisonment or even the death sentence for looting. (IWM HU 36177)

Aldwych tube station during the blitz, with Londoners reduced to trying to make a bed between the rails. (IWM HU44272)

J.B. Priestley was second only to Churchill in his popularity as a radio broadcaster during the war, but he was dropped by the BBC for his views about the aims of the war and what should happen afterwards. He is seen here (left) with actor Leslie Howard. (IWM HU 36268)

Women were not allowed to join the Home Guard, but some of them were good enough shots to train the Home Guards in shooting. Some of them set up their own organisation – the Amazons Defence Corps. They are seen here practising in Hillingdon. (IWM HU 36270)

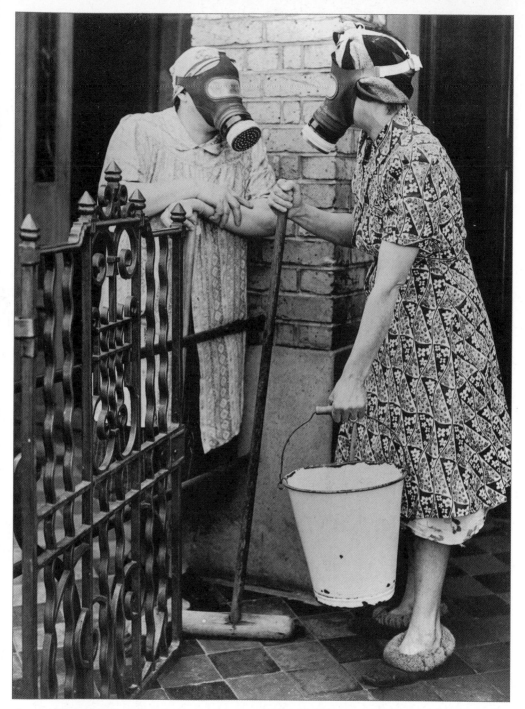

Gas-masks did for the art of conversation . . . well, they did for the art of conversation full stop. This was a contrived photograph for propaganda purposes, taken in Southend in 1941. As the war went on, the general public were much less likely to carry, let alone to wear, their gas-masks. (IWM HU 36137)

May 1940, and female aliens are unceremoniously rounded up and taken under police escort to an internment camp in the Isle of Man. Their male counterparts had an armed military escort and some faced hostile crowds en route. (IWM HU 36121)

Russian Ambassador Ivan Maisky accepts the first tank to be delivered in the 'Tanks for Russia' programme. Our alliance with the Russians was in some ways a considerable embarrassment to the wartime government. (IWM HU 57227)

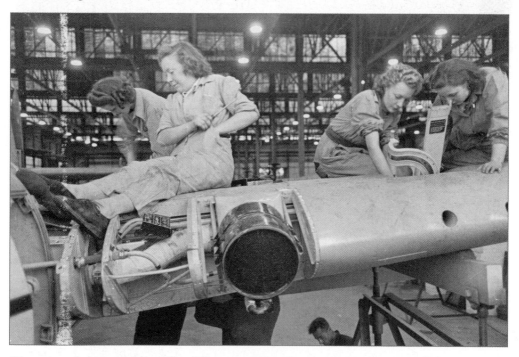

Women workers assemble a Beaufighter in 1941. Having made a huge contribution to the wartime economy, many of the advances women made in the field of employment were lost at the end of the war. (IWM L84)

Hitler's *V-weapons* brought a new reign of terror to London in the last years of the war. A *V2* rocket fell on Smithfield Market on 9 March 1945 and here rescue workers pick their way through the wreckage with a badly injured woman.
(IWM HU 65896)